DINOSAURS

DINOSAURS

THE WORLD'S MOST TERRIFYING CREATURES

General Editor: Veronica Ross

amber
BOOKS

First published in 2005 by
Amber Books Ltd
74–77 White Lion Street
London
N1 9PF
United Kingdom
www.amberbooks.co.uk

ISBN 1-904687-30-X

Printed and bound in Italy

Project Editor: Tom Broder
Designer: Joe Conneally

Contents

Introduction

Eustreptospondylus

Edmontonia

Ornitholestes

The name dinosaur means 'very terrible lizard'. No human being has ever seen a real live dinosaur. This is because dinosaurs lived on Earth millions of years before we did. Even so, we do know a lot about them. Many dinosaur bones, teeth or fossils have been found all over the world. Fossils are impressions or marks made in rocks by the bodies of animals or plants which died very long ago. From the evidence of these fossils, scientists have worked out what dinosaurs looked like, how they moved and what – or who – they ate.

There were many different kinds of dinosaurs. Some were enormous. The *Iguanodon*, one of the first dinosaurs to be discovered, was up to 10 metres long. But there were also tiny dinosaurs. *Compsognathus* looked like a bird, with a small, pointed head and a long neck, and was about the size of a chicken. Some dinosaurs, such as *Iguanodon*, walked around on two legs. Others,

Dilophosaurus

Styracosaurus

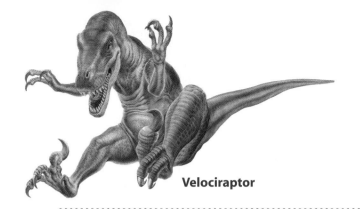

Velociraptor

Triceratops

Parasaurolophus

such as *Triceratops*, a dinosaur with horns, moved about on four. Some ate plants, others were ferocious meat-eaters.

Not all dinosaurs lived at the same time. The first appeared on Earth some 205 million years ago: the last lived around 65 million years ago. During these 140 million years, the Earth went through three main eras, or ages: the Triassic, the Jurassic and the Cretaceous. Then, it seems, the dinosaurs died out. There are many explanations for this. Some scientists blame disease or erupting volcanoes. Others blame changes caused by the impact of a huge asteroid from space.

The dinosaurs were not the only creatures to live on Earth at this time. Many other weird and wonderful creatures, from giant sharks to sabre-toothed cats, shared the prehistoric world. Some existed long before the dinosaurs, some lived alongside the dinosaurs, and others were around long after the last of the dinosaurs had died out.

Deinocheirus

Suchomimus

Before the Dinosaurs

Strange and bloodthirsty beasts prowled the Earth long before the time of the dinosaurs. Some of these creatures were the ancestors of the dinosaurs. Others looked more like they came from another world.

The earliest dinosaurs lived over 200 million years ago. But, even before the first dinosaur walked the Earth, the world was full of all sorts of weird and wonderful beasts.

Among these creatures were some fearsome reptiles that looked very much like dinosaurs, such as the vicious lizard *Dimetrodon*. Other creatures included *Diplocaulus*, a strange-looking animal with a head like a boomerang, and *Dunkleosteus*, a huge prehistoric fish with a mouthful of sharp teeth. Living even earlier than these beasts, before animals had begun to move out of the seas and on to dry land, were bizarre and alien-looking sea creatures such as trilobites and eurypterids.

Then, about 248 million years ago, at the end of the Permian age, something terrible happened: a mass extinction killed so many creatures that life itself almost came to an end. It is thought that up to 95 per cent of sea creatures were destroyed and up to 78 per cent of reptiles. Happily, a few creatures did survive. Among them were reptiles that would later become the dinosaurs.

TRILOBITE

BODY

The body had three sections: a *cephalon* (head), thorax (body) and *pygidium* (tail).

LEGS

The jointed legs bristled with spines. Some of them were used to aid walking, others to seize and tear up prey. On each limb were feathery filaments that served as gills to take oxygen from the water.

EYES

The solid crystal eyes are unique in the natural world. They appeared in many shapes and sizes.

ANTENNAE

These were the 'ears' and 'nose', essential for sensing food and danger in dark waters.

Trilobites scuttled about the seabeds of the ancient world like weird prehistoric crabs, finally dying out shortly before the dinosaurs began their rule. Fossils show that they existed in vast numbers and in a huge variety of forms and sizes — the smallest were about 1mm long.

Trilobites evolved long before flowering plants, dinosaurs, fish and mammals, and are almost as old as time itself. They developed the earliest known eyes, made from solid crystal. Trilobites were so successful that they barely changed during the course of 300 million years.

HOW BIG WAS IT?

DINO FACTS

LENGTH	1mm–40cm	
SEGMENTS	2 to 44	
EYES	Up to 15,000 lenses per eye	
DIET	Plankton, worms, other trilobites	
ENEMIES	Other trilobites, jawed fishes	
MEANING OF NAME	'Three lobes'	

Trilobites occurred in every sea and ocean, from shallows to dark depths and from icy polar waters to the warm tropics. Throughout their long existence, the land masses were constantly on the move.

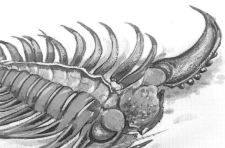

1 A tiny *Acidaspis*, only 1cm long, is undergoing one of its regular moults. Its exoskeleton splits and cracks along joints known as *sutures*.

2 Freshly emerged, the *Acidaspis* has shed all protection from its body, antennae, legs and spines. Now its soft inner body has room to grow a little.

3 But before the new exoskeleton can harden, a prowling *Huntonia trilobite* nips in for the kill. The *Huntonia* clasps the little *Acidaspis* and shreds the victim with the vicious spikes at the base of its legs.

Did You Know?

● One reason why trilobite fossils are so common is that the animals shed their exoskeletons regularly as they grew, and the exoskeletons also often became fossils.

● The first scientists to study trilobites 300 years ago thought that they were a kind of flatfish.

● The closest living relative of the trilobite is the horseshoe crab of North American and Asian coasts.

● The fossil trilobite *Drepanura* is called the 'swallow stone' in China, where people grind it up and add it to a potion believed to prolong life.

EURYPTERID

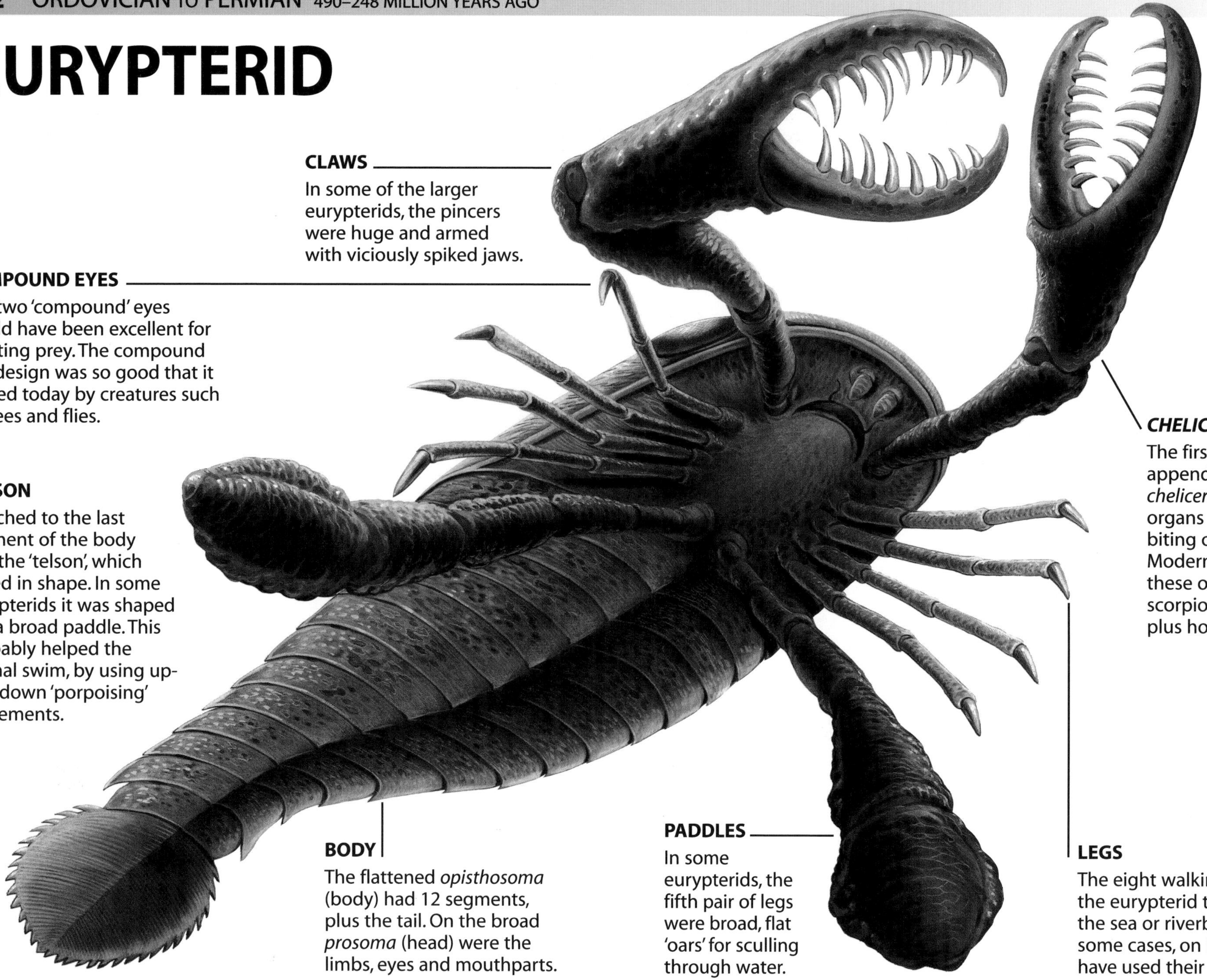

CLAWS

In some of the larger eurypterids, the pincers were huge and armed with viciously spiked jaws.

COMPOUND EYES

The two 'compound' eyes would have been excellent for spotting prey. The compound eye design was so good that it is used today by creatures such as bees and flies.

TELSON

Attached to the last segment of the body was the 'telson', which varied in shape. In some eurypterids it was shaped like a broad paddle. This probably helped the animal swim, by using up-and-down 'porpoising' movements.

CHELICERAE

The first pair of appendages are the *chelicerae*: pincer-like organs for seizing, biting or crushing prey. Modern animals with these organs include all scorpions and spiders, plus horseshoe crabs.

BODY

The flattened *opisthosoma* (body) had 12 segments, plus the tail. On the broad *prosoma* (head) were the limbs, eyes and mouthparts.

PADDLES

In some eurypterids, the fifth pair of legs were broad, flat 'oars' for sculling through water.

LEGS

The eight walking legs helped the eurypterid to walk across the sea or riverbed — and, in some cases, on land. Some may have used their legs to trap prey.

Eurypterids belonged to an incredibly successful animal group that survived for around 250 million years. They were scorpion-like water creatures that hunted fish and other prey. Giant eurypterids, larger than modern-day humans and equipped with huge claws for crushing their victims, were among the most fearsome predators of their day.

Some types were probably the first among the ancient animals to move between water and dry land. Early eurypterids lived in the seas, but fossil trackways prove that they also could crawl on to beaches. As well as large gills for breathing underwater, they also had a second set of small gills which allowed them to breathe in air.

HOW BIG WAS IT?

In many eurypterids, the last pair of legs were strong paddles. They used these to chase fast-swimming fish, or to swim to good feeding sites.

1

DINO FACTS

LENGTH	From a few cm to more than 2m in the largest (*Pterygotus buffaloensis*).
DIET	Other invertebrates and, in the larger species, fish.
MEANING OF NAME	'Wide wings', referring to the paddle-like hindlimbs

Eurypterids roamed widely, but most fossils come from eastern North America and western Europe. This map shows the location of the ancient shallow seas where many of them lived.

Eurypterids could scuttle along the sea floor on their strong walking legs. In some species, these limbs were very sturdy. In others, they were long and slender, to help their owner walk across soft mud or sand.

2

Did You Know?

● At the last count, scientists list around 300 species of eurypterid, dividing them into 22 families.

● Eurypterids had their heyday in the Silurian and Devonian periods (about 410–360 million years ago). They vanished shortly before the dinosaurs appeared, during a mass extinction that affected many other creatures as well.

● During the times in which they lived, eurypterids were probably the largest animals in the world.

● The eurypterid *Eurypterus remipes* was chosen as the official state fossil of New York in 1984. Fossils of this species are among the most common in New York State – which in fact is one of the world's best places to find eurypterids.

COELACANTH

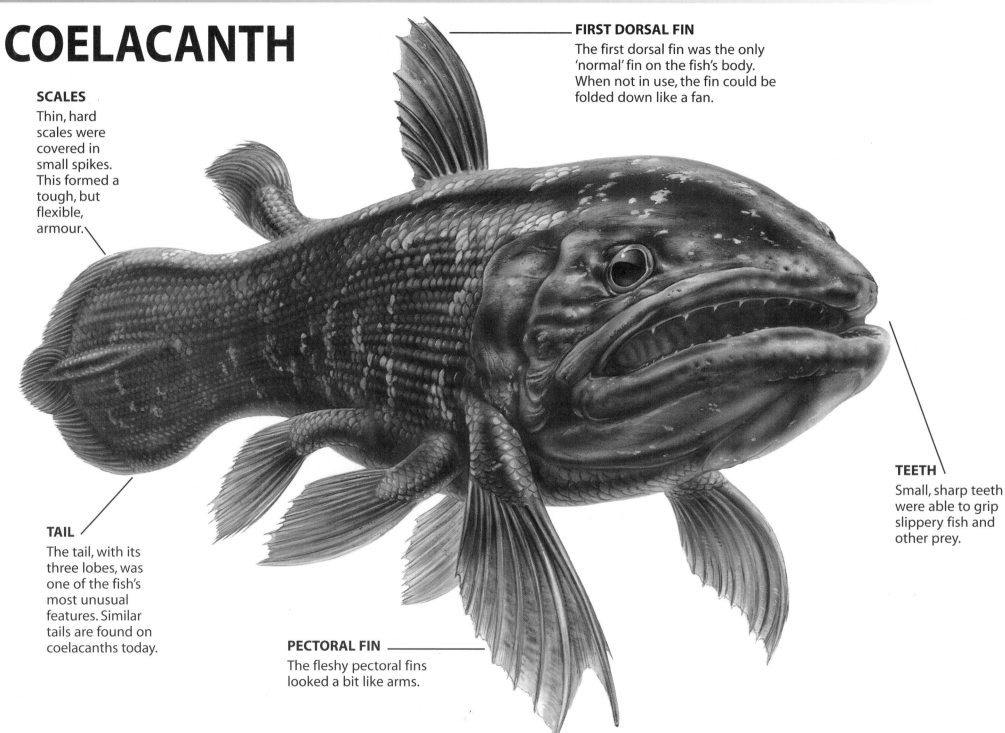

SCALES
Thin, hard scales were covered in small spikes. This formed a tough, but flexible, armour.

FIRST DORSAL FIN
The first dorsal fin was the only 'normal' fin on the fish's body. When not in use, the fin could be folded down like a fan.

TEETH
Small, sharp teeth were able to grip slippery fish and other prey.

TAIL
The tail, with its three lobes, was one of the fish's most unusual features. Similar tails are found on coelacanths today.

PECTORAL FIN
The fleshy pectoral fins looked a bit like arms.

This odd-looking deep-sea fish first prowled the prehistoric seas over 400 million years ago, long before the age of the dinosaurs. And, unlike dinosaurs, the coelacanth still survives today. A live coelacanth was caught off South Africa in 1938, and more have been found since.

Its rediscovery caused a sensation among scientists, who had believed that it was extinct. The modern coelacanth's internal organs are unlike those of any other modern animals, and its bone structure is just like that of ancient fossils.

The spinal cord is known as a *notochord*, and was simply a flexible tube filled with fluid (1). In more advanced fish and vertebrates, this is enclosed by vertebrae to form a backbone.

HOW BIG WAS IT?

The pectoral fins were connected to a supporting bone structure called the 'pectoral girdle' (2), just like human legs connect to the pelvic girdle. This made the fins very manoeuvrable.

DINO FACTS

LENGTH	Up to 1.8m; average 1m
WEIGHT	Up to 80kg
FOOD	Smaller fish
BREEDING	Incubated fertilised eggs inside its body
LIFESPAN	Around 11 years (female)

The first modern coelacanth were discovered in the deep ocean water off Africa (*see map*), but their prehistoric counterparts were probably freshwater dwellers. Coleacanth fossils have been discovered in Europe and North and South America.

The skull was divided into two separate compartments, joined by a hinge. The eyes and teeth were in the front part. The back section contained the tiny brain. A fold in the skin marked the join (3).

Did You Know?

● A coelacanth's brain filled just 1.5 per cent of the available skull space.

● Modern coelacanth eggs can be as big as tennis balls. The female keeps them inside her body until they hatch, then gives birth to baby fish.

● The modern coelacanth's heart is just an S-shaped tube, while the kidneys are fused together to make one organ. This kidney structure is unique among vertebrates today.

Each leg-like fin had a complex skeleton (4), with several moveable bones connected to strong muscles. All these fins were very mobile, and could probably rotate backwards and forwards, or move up and down.

DUNKLEOSTEUS

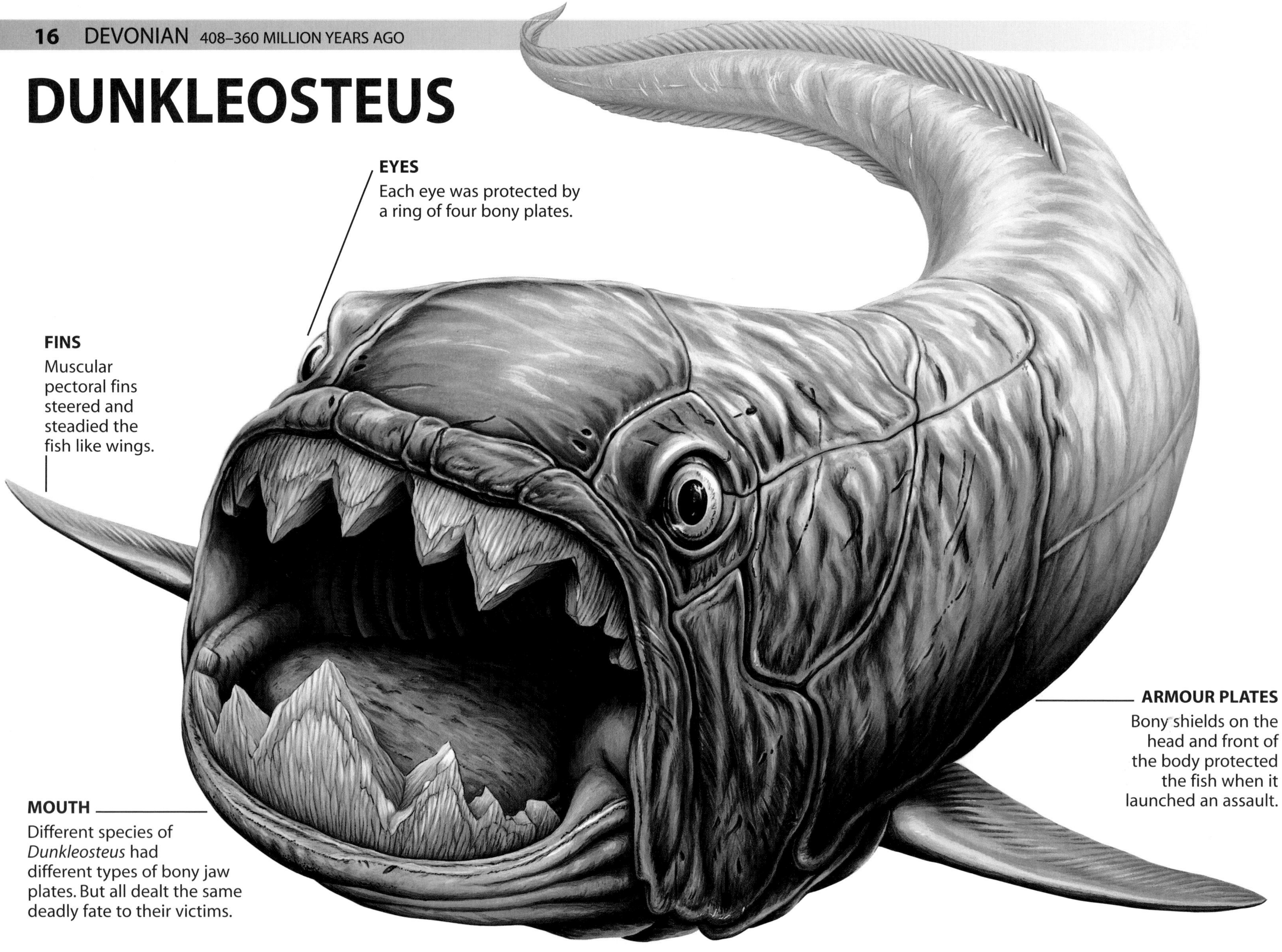

EYES
Each eye was protected by
a ring of four bony plates.

FINS
Muscular
pectoral fins
steered and
steadied the
fish like wings.

ARMOUR PLATES
Bony shields on the
head and front of
the body protected
the fish when it
launched an assault.

MOUTH
Different species of
Dunkleosteus had
different types of bony jaw
plates. But all dealt the same
deadly fate to their victims.

This colossal fish would have spread panic among the other creatures in the prehistoric seas. Its massive mouth was filled with huge, slicing knives of bone. It could fling both jaws open wide to bite many of its victims clean in half.

Dunkleosteus had a great head encased in bony armour plates, and a muscular body that stretched several metres. This terrifying creature searched far and wide for prey, ready to snap at any fish that swam within reach.

HOW BIG WAS IT?

DINO FACTS

LENGTH	Possibly up to 6m
WEIGHT	Up to 1 tonne or more
PREY	Mainly fish
MEANING OF NAME	'Dunkle's bones' (after the man who first described it)

Fossilized *Dunkleosteus* bones have been found in the USA, Morocco and Germany. When the fish lived, eastern North America, Europe and northern Africa were joined beneath a shallow tropical sea.

1 A primitive fish called *Holocephalans* is about to meet a sudden end. Out of the gloom, *Dunkleosteus* rushes forth, alerted by motion sensors in its sides. Close up, the predator's big eyes guide it into the attack.

2 *Holocephalans* desperately tries to escape, but its efforts are futile. *Dunkleosteus* swings open its cavernous jaws and with one brutal bite shears its victim in two.

Did You Know?

● *Dunkleosteus* is the largest of no fewer than 22 species of arthrodires (joint-necked armoured fish) found as fossils in the Cleveland Shale of Ohio, USA. Also found in these ancient rocks are the remains of a great many other fish, including primitive sharks and coelacanths.

● Many of the early joint-necked armoured fishes and some of the later forms were not at all like the dashing *Dunkleosteus*. They were sluggish fish that nosed their way through the bottom sediments.

● The bony cutting blades in *Dunkleosteus*'s mouth grew slowly throughout its life. The constant meshing action between the two sets of blades wore them back, regulating their length and keeping them wickedly sharp.

COELUROSAURAVUS

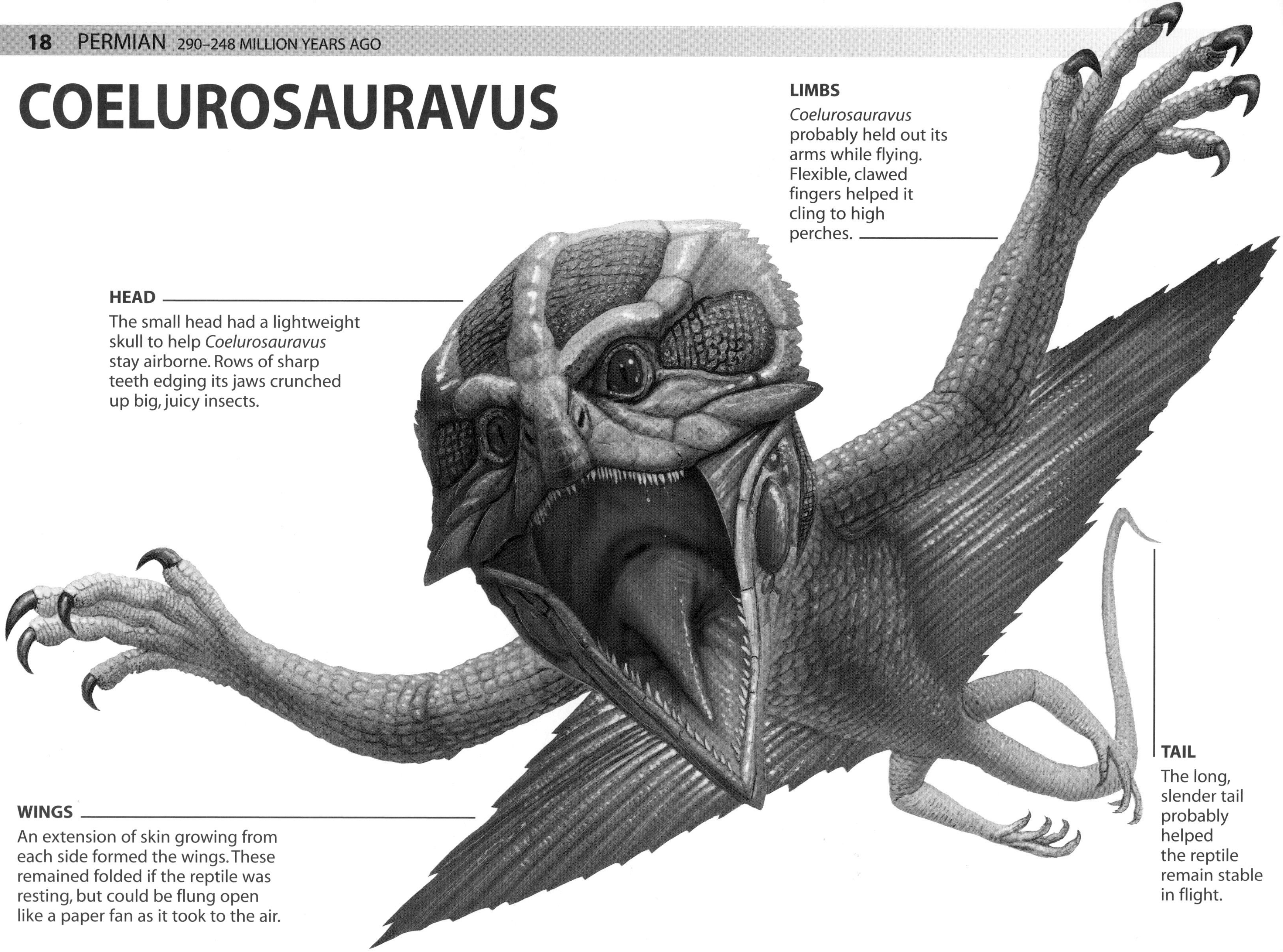

LIMBS

Coelurosauravus probably held out its arms while flying. Flexible, clawed fingers helped it cling to high perches.

HEAD

The small head had a lightweight skull to help *Coelurosauravus* stay airborne. Rows of sharp teeth edging its jaws crunched up big, juicy insects.

TAIL

The long, slender tail probably helped the reptile remain stable in flight.

WINGS

An extension of skin growing from each side formed the wings. These remained folded if the reptile was resting, but could be flung open like a paper fan as it took to the air.

This unique flying reptile probably lived in forests and preyed on big insects. It may also have hunted and rested in small flocks like some modern birds. *Coelurosauravus* is the earliest known flying vertebrate (backboned animal). It had foldable wings supported by hollow, bony struts.

Its wings, which were constructed like two paper fans, helped it to glide from tree to tree using its tail as a rudder to steer. It may also have spread its wings to raise its temperature by basking in the sun.

HOW BIG WAS IT?

1 It is morning. A flock of lizards cling to a giant tree, their wings extended to soak up the sunshine.

DINO FACTS

LENGTH	30–40cm	A copper miner in England discovered the first fossilized remains of *Coelurosauravus* in 1910. Since then, further specimens have been unearthed in Madagascar off the eastern coast of Africa, in England and, in the late 1980s, in the Kupershiefer formation of eastern Germany.
WINGSPAN	30cm	
LIFESTYLE	Lived in trees	
PREY	Insects	
MEANING OF NAME	'Hollow-boned lizard bird'	

As the sun arcs across the sky, a shadow falls across their perch. The group leaps into the air and flits across to another tree still in the sun.

2

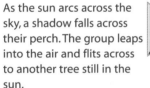

Did You Know?

● *Coelurosauravus* and its close relatives the coelurosauravids came from a separate evolutionary group to the ancient lizards. The ancestors of the two groups split from one another early in the Permian period.

● *Coelurosauravus* was one of many prehistoric victims of a mass extinction that occurred about 250 million years ago. Its unique wing design seems to have died out with it, for, as far as we know, no other flying vertebrate has developed a similar structure since then.

● When *Coelurosauravus* was at large, the only other creatures in the air were flying insects. It took at least another 20 million years for the next gliding reptile to evolve, and many more million years passed before the first birds and bats appeared.

DIMETRODON

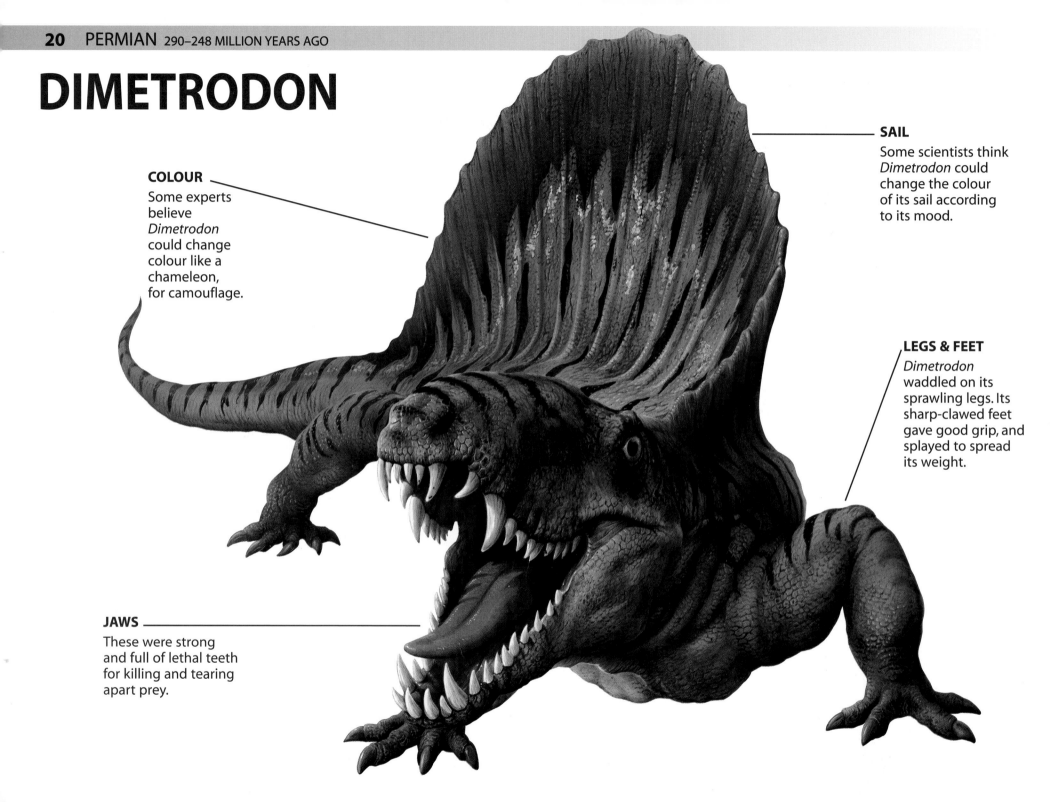

SAIL
Some scientists think *Dimetrodon* could change the colour of its sail according to its mood.

COLOUR
Some experts believe *Dimetrodon* could change colour like a chameleon, for camouflage.

LEGS & FEET
Dimetrodon waddled on its sprawling legs. Its sharp-clawed feet gave good grip, and splayed to spread its weight.

JAWS
These were strong and full of lethal teeth for killing and tearing apart prey.

A fearsome beast with a huge arching sail on its back and a vicious set of teeth, *Dimetrodon* stalked the Earth more than 260 million years ago and was probably the top predator on land at that time. It would have killed its prey with crushing bites from its stabbing fangs and sliced off flesh using its razor-sharp teeth.

The strange sail on its back was probably used to help it take in heat from the sun. This would have warmed the reptile up quickly after a cold night and given it a head start on its victims.

HOW BIG WAS IT?

At dawn, *Dimetrodon* turns its sail to face the rising sun. Blood coursing through the veins in the thin skin of the sail warms quickly.

1

Within half an hour, *Dimetrodon* is warm enough to run about. Soon the creature picks up the scent trail of a large reptile, *Ophiacodon*.

2

Ophiacodon has no sail, so is still warming itself slowly. It is so cold and slow it can not even run away as *Dimetrodon*'s teeth sink into its back.

3

DINO FACTS

LENGTH	Up to 3.5m from snout to tip of tail	Fossil *Dimetrodon* remains have been found in Texas, New Mexico and Oklahoma in the USA. When the reptile was alive, the world's continents were joined in one huge land mass, which scientists call *Pangaea*. This may mean *Dimetrodon* had a much larger range than fossil finds indicate.
HEIGHT	Up to 2m to top of sail	
WEIGHT	Up to 250kg	
PREY	Other reptiles, large and small, and possibly also fish, shellfish and any carrion it came across	
MEANING OF NAME	'Two sizes of teeth'	

Did You Know?

● *Dimetrodon* was a kind of mammal-like reptile called a 'pelycosaur', and as such was more closely related to humans and other mammals than to dinosaurs.

● *Dimetrodon* did not even share the Earth with dinosaurs. It became extinct some 35 million years before the earliest dinosaurs existed.

● One early theory put forward to explain the purpose of *Dimetrodon*'s sail was that it was a camouflage device to hide the reptile in swamp plants. Another idea was that it was an actual sail to catch the wind and help the creature swim.

DIPLOCAULUS

TAIL
A powerful tail would have helped drive *Diplocaulus* through the water at great speed.

BODY
The long, flattened body would have enabled the animal to lie in ambush on the water bottom.

LEGS
The legs were short and fairly weak. They were useful for steering in water and for crawling through mud, but not very good on dry land.

EYES
Large eyes set high on its head would have helped *Diplocaulus* watch for prey on the water surface.

HEAD
The unusual triangular shape of the head was formed by two greatly elongated bones at the back of the skull that stuck out from the sides.

MOUTH
The small mouth was lined with rows of razor-sharp teeth for slicing bite-size chunks of flesh from prey.

A killer amphibian that once lived in swampy North America, *Diplocaulus* was able to walk on land, but was also a good swimmer. It could probably survive long periods underwater. It may have lain partly concealed in the mud and stones at the bottom of waterways, waiting for prey, such as insects or fish to pass by.

Some experts think that it may have used its boomerang-shaped head to help it speed through the water to chase prey. The head might have protected it from predators too; even the hungriest hunter would have found its large shape hard to swallow.

HOW BIG WAS IT?

DINO FACTS

SIZE	About 1.3m long with a head some 40cm wide	*Diplocaulus* fossils have mainly been found in the US states of Texas and Oklahoma. When this amphibian was alive, the region was wet and swampy, and crisscrossed with many lakes and rivers – quite different from the arid region it is today. Fossils of amphibians similar in shape to *Diplocaulus* have been discovered in Morocco.
WEIGHT	Possibly up to 15kg	
PREY	Probably mainly fish and insects	
MEANING OF NAME	'Double stalk'	

Two *Diplocaulus* race to grab a huge dragonfly that has crashed on the water and is struggling to get airborne.

1

The amphibians close their jaws round the insect in a grisly tug-of-war. The long dragonfly tears apart, and each *Diplocaulus* wolfs down its share. They return to the bottom of the water to wait for more prey.

2

Did You Know?

● Young *Diplocaulus* did not have the triangular head of the adults. The bones at the back of the head that formed the 'boomerang' shape grew slowly as the animal matured, becoming much bigger with age.

● Experts think *Diplocaulus* laid eggs in water, as many amphibians do today. The eggs would have hatched into tadpoles that stayed in the water while they grew into adults.

● Another amphibian of the same period, called *Diploceraspis*, also had a hugely expanded skull, which suggests that an odd head shape was a useful adaptation that gave these creatures a clear advantage.

● *Diplocaulus* may have had gills to enable it to breathe underwater as it lay still, watching for prey.

The Triassic Period

A great extinction took place at the start of the Triassic period, killing most of the Earth's creatures. Only a few animals survived, but among them were the great reptiles that would become the dinosaurs.

It was during the Triassic period that the first proper dinosaurs began to appear, such as *Coelophysis*, a fast, vicious dinosaur that lived and hunted in packs. Many dinosaurs of the Triassic period were carnivores (meat-eaters). They stood on two legs and were very fast on their feet when hunting for their food. They had huge mouths full of large, sharp teeth. They needed these teeth and also their powerful claws as weapons to kill, then eat their prey. One Triassic age dinosaur, *Herrerasaurus,* was an early ancestor of the most fearsome dinosaur of them all: *Tyrannosaurus rex.* With dinosaurs such as this around, the world in the Triassic period was a very dangerous place.

The dinosaurs were not the only big reptiles of the period. One fearsome Triassic predator was *Cynognathus*, a large mammal-like reptile that looked like a cross between a dog and a lizard. Another big dinosaur-like reptile, called *Postosuchus*, was actually the ancestor of modern crocodiles. But by the end of the Triassic period it was clear that it was dinosaurs which now dominated the Earth.

COELOPHYSIS

NECK
A flexible neck helped the dino to reach out and grab prey.

HANDS
Coelophysis may have used its clawed hands to dig small mammals out of their burrows.

EYES & NOSE
Forward-facing eyes and keen nostrils helped the beast pinpoint its next bloody meal.

TEETH
The dagger-like teeth were made for ripping into flesh, not dining daintily on leaves.

Oने of the earliest known dinosaurs, *Coelophysis* was a highly efficient killer. It could hunt down prey with great speed and agility, before tucking in hungrily with its sharp, snapping teeth. This avid meat-eater may even have feasted on its own young.

With its streamlined shape, lightweight skeleton and long, muscular legs, *Coelophysis* was a born runner. It could turn and twist at top speed. A pack of these dinosaurs could have brought down prey a great deal bigger than themselves.

HOW BIG WAS IT?

DINO FACTS

LENGTH	About 3m	Fossilized *Coelophysis* remains are known from deposits in Arizona and New Mexico in the USA. The world's land formed one gigantic supercontinent, known as Pangaea, when *Coelophysis* was alive. The climate was warm or hot all year round, and *Coelophysis* may have roamed far and wide in search of prey.
WEIGHT	About 25kg	
DIET	Other animals, dead or alive	
WEAPONS	Teeth and claws	
MEANING OF NAME	'Hollow form' (because it had hollow bones)	

1 As some young and adult *Coelophysis* feed nervously from a carcass, a rival pack of adults sneak up close.

2 Springing from cover, the hungry adults surge into the attack. They snatch up some of the smaller youngsters, then flee into the forest.

Did You Know?

● The Ghost Ranch site in New Mexico is a rich fossil site. Vast numbers of *Coelophysis* fossils have been found, and there may be as many as 1000 yet to be excavated.

● Not all adult *Coelophysis* fossil remains are the same, for there are two forms of the dinosaur, one larger than the other. Experts think these represent males and females, but there is still much debate over which are which.

● US fossil hunter Edward Drinker Cope named *Coelophysis* in 1887, based on fragmentary remains.

● Fossil experts estimate that in the mid-Triassic, when *Coelophysis* roamed, dinosaurs accounted for less than 5 per cent of the different species of reptile in the world.

CYNOGNATHUS

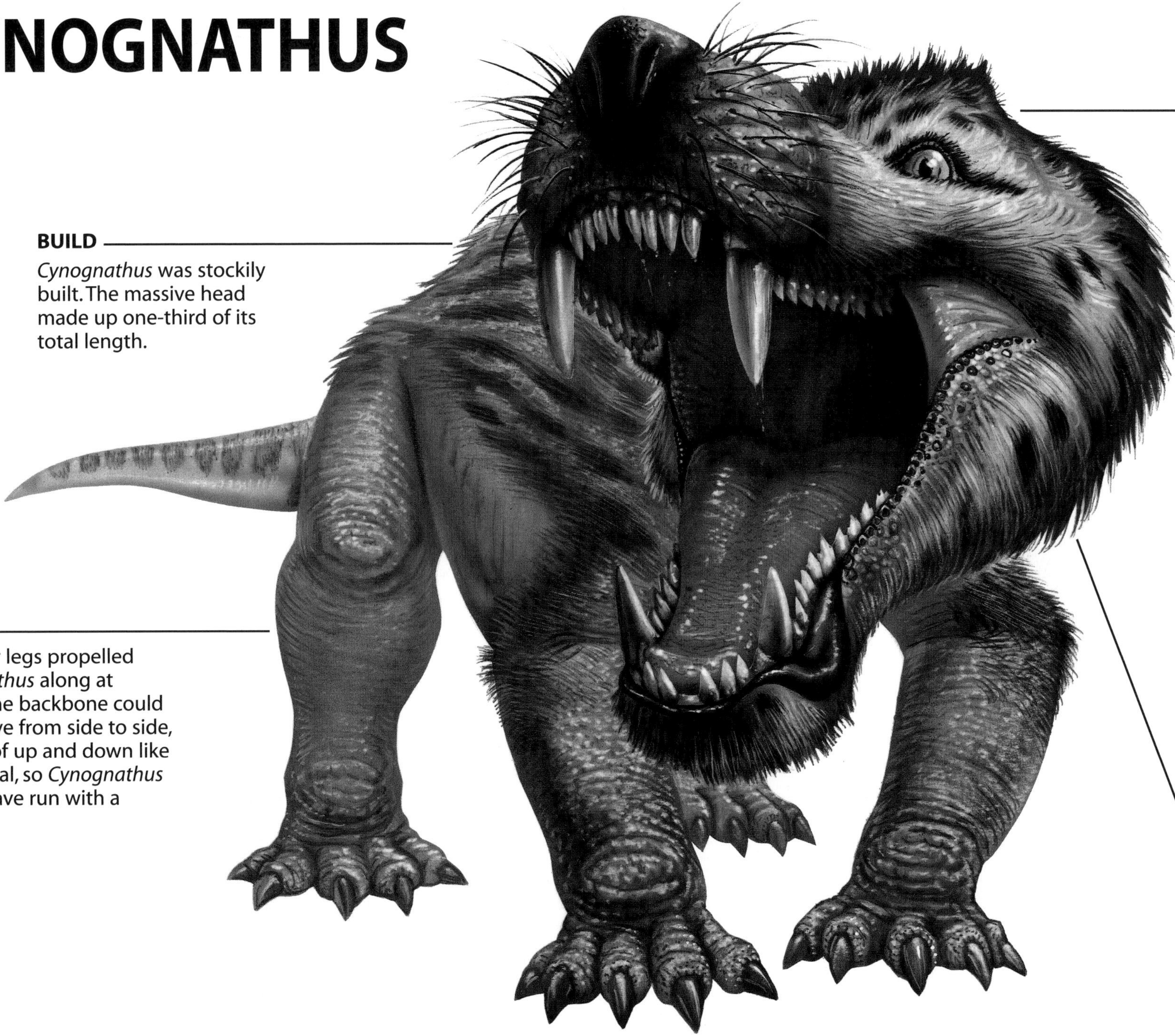

FUR

The body was covered in fur to prevent heat loss during the cold nights.

BUILD

Cynognathus was stockily built. The massive head made up one-third of its total length.

LEGS

Muscular legs propelled *Cynognathus* along at speed. The backbone could only move from side to side, instead of up and down like a mammal, so *Cynognathus* would have run with a waddle.

JAWS

Huge and powerful jaws opened wide. Sharp canines and nipping incisor teeth pierced blood vessels and ripped flesh.

Cynognathus looked like a cross between a dog and a lizard. It was the biggest of all the cynodonts, mammal-like reptiles equipped with vicious fangs. When hunting in a pack, *Cynognathus* was deadly, killing much larger animals and ripping them to shreds.

Unlike most true reptiles, *Cynognathus* had relatively long legs that were positioned under its body instead of sticking out at the sides. This meant that it was agile on its feet and could change direction quickly. Fossilized remains of this carnivore have helped scientists to understand how mammals evolved.

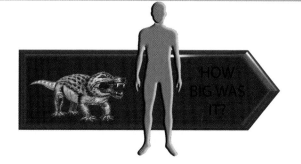

HOW BIG WAS IT?

DINO FACTS

LENGTH	1–1.5m in total; snouted head 30cm	
DIET	Fresh meat	
WEAPONS	Fearsome teeth and ripping claws	*Cynognathus* fossils were first found in Argentina (1) and in South Africa's Karoo Basin (2), a great desert-like bowl of scrub-covered rock. More were found near Beijing, China (3), in 1973.
MEANING OF NAME	'Dog-jawed'	

1 Three *Cynognathus* attack a large *Kannemeyeria*. One sinks its fangs into the victim's throat. The second springs on to its back and another lunges at its belly.

Did You Know?

● The only evidence that suggests *Cynognathus* and other cynodonts were furry comes from a fur imprint around a single fossilized footprint.

● Fossil records do not tell us how *Cynognathus* reproduced, but at some stage cynodonts changed from laying eggs to giving birth to live young.

● In 1912, after studying fossilized *Cynognathus* and *Mesosaurus* remains from South America and Africa, the German scientist Alfred Wegener concluded that the two landmasses were once joined together, and had drifted into their current positions over many millions of years.

● Some cynodont skulls have tiny canals in the area around the snout, and these may have contained the sensory nerves of whisker-like hairs.

2 Despite its great bulk, *Kannemeyeria* can not shake off its attackers. It finally keels over. The smaller dinosaurs rip out its guts.

GRACILISUCHUS

EYES

Gracilisuchus had big eyes. This suggests the animal hunted mainly by sight.

JAWS

The long and well-muscled jaws would have held the reptile's victims in a vice-like grip.

TEETH

These were shaped like blades. They were perfect for slicing clean through small prey or biting chunks of flesh from large animal carcasses.

FORELIMBS

The forelimbs were just two-thirds the length of the hindlimbs. They ended in long razor-sharp claws.

L iving among the earliest dinosaurs was a fast little reptile capable of snatching fish from water, chasing lizards on land and even plucking insects out of the air.

Gracilisuchus was a long-legged predator that mainly raced about on all fours, but could also run on its hindlegs balanced by its long tail. Its nimble limbs, large eyes and long claws made this reptile a viciously efficient predator. It would have been able to hunt a wide variety of animals or grab meat from bigger killers and run off with it.

HOW BIG WAS IT?

DINO FACTS

LENGTH	45–50cm, including 9.5cm skull	*Gracilisuchus'* fossils were found in northern Argentina. About 230 million years ago, this region was part of the giant supercontinent of Pangaea. The climate slowly changed from being warm and moist to hot and dry, and the dominant vegetation switched from ferns to conifers. Many new animals appeared, including *Gracilisuchus*.
DIET	Probably small lizards, insects, fish and carrion	
WEAPONS	Teeth and claws	
MEANING OF NAME	'Graceful crocodile'	

Gracilisuchus crouches at a pool to drink. The killer sees a shoal of tiny fish and snaps at them with its jaws. But the fish are too quick and escape.

1

2 *Gracilisuchus* runs off to try its luck elsewhere. It sees a dragonfly and leaps into the air to try to catch the insect. But it has no success.

Did You Know?

● Along with *Gracilisuchus*, many other types of early crocodile-like creatures lived in the Triassic period. They included *Parasuchus*, which had a long, slender snout like a modern crocodile, and the *rauisuchians*, which at up to 7m long were the major killers of their day.

● *Gracilisuchus'* spinal bones were protected by pairs of interlocking armour plates. Some experts think they protected the spine, but others believe they helped to stiffen the body and so improve balance.

● Alfred Romer first described *Gracilisuchus* in 1972. It resembled *Ornithosuchus*, another Triassic reptile, which some experts thought was a dinosaur. Romer disagreed, and research has since proved him right: neither animal was a dinosaur.

Some distance away, *Gracilisuchus* spots some other dinosaurs with a fresh kill. The two dinosaurs are too busy feeding to spot the agile little intruder. The raider runs in and steals a lump of bloody flesh.

3

HERRERASAURUS

COLOUR

No one knows what colour dinosaurs were, but it is likely that this dinosaur would have had camouflage markings. This would have helped it to hide in the undergrowth.

HEAD

The long, narrow head allowed the animal to reach deep inside a dead carcass to feast on the juicy internal organs.

LOWER JAW

Herrerasaurus had a special hinge on its jaw, which allowed the animal to hold its prey in an unbreakable grip.

TAIL

The dinosaur held its long tail well off the ground. This way, thr tail helped balance the body.

CLAWS

These were surprisingly sharp and powerful. The beast may have used them to pin down struggling prey.

TEETH

The teeth were curved and pointed. They were powerful enough to penetrate a victim's skull.

F ast and ferocious, this lion-sized meat-eater was one of the first in a long line of two-legged predators that would eventually lead to the king of killers: *Tyrannosaurus rex*.

Herrerasaurus is one of the oldest known dinosaurs. Its appearance marked the start of the age when the dinosaurs reigned supreme and slower four-legged killers lost out in the battle for survival. The mighty beast had sharp teeth and claws, and its lower jaw was hinged, which gave it a huge, vice-like bite.

HOW BIG WAS IT?

DINO FACTS

SIZE	Length up to 3m, including tail; weight 100–180kg	*Herrerasaurus* fossils have been found in the San Juan region of Argentina, in the foothills of the Andean mountains, close to the Chilean border. When the dinosaurs roamed, 220 million years ago, this area was part of the continent of Pangaea, Earth's climate was hotter than today, and great deserts and forests were widespread.
DIET	Dinosaurs and other reptiles; possibly carrion	
WEAPONS	Sharp teeth and claws	
MEANING OF NAME	'Herrera's lizard'	

1 A young *Herrerasaurus* takes advantage of the easy meal provided by a dead plant-eater. Head down, the hunter tears off great strips of flesh. But a larger *Herrerasaurus* is drawn to the meal. It attacks the younger animal, biting its head.

2 The smaller predator shrieks with pain and slinks away to hide until its wounds have healed. The victorious animal bends down and eagerly begins to feed.

Did You Know?

● *Herrerasaurus* was named after Victorino Herrera, the Andean farmer who discovered its fossil remains.

● Some scientists think predatory dinosaurs such as *Herrerasaurus* lived in packs and fought with each other for dominance. Partly healed tooth marks on the skulls of such dinosaurs show they bit each other on the head, like wolves do today.

● *Herrerasaurus'* forelimbs were quite powerful and had hooked claws. The predator may have used them to slash at prey animals in the hope of delivering a mortal wound.

● Having studied the foot bones of *Herrerasaurus*, some fossil experts claim it is not a true dino, but lies somewhere between the dinosaurs and their more primitive ancestors.

LYSTROSAURUS

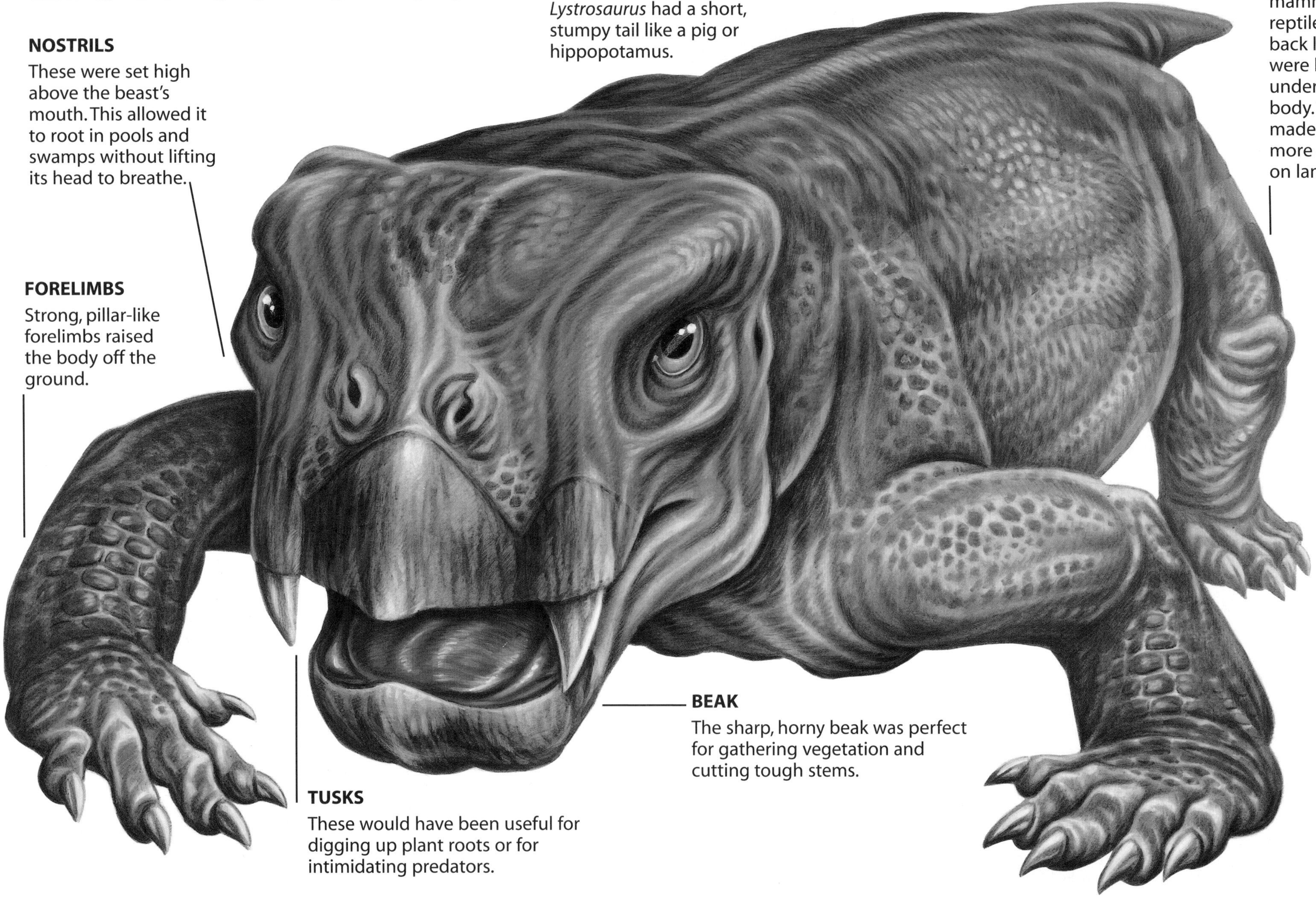

NOSTRILS

These were set high above the beast's mouth. This allowed it to root in pools and swamps without lifting its head to breathe.

FORELIMBS

Strong, pillar-like forelimbs raised the body off the ground.

TAIL

Lystrosaurus had a short, stumpy tail like a pig or hippopotamus.

HINDLIMBS

As with all mammal-like reptiles, the back legs were held under the body. This made it more agile on land.

TUSKS

These would have been useful for digging up plant roots or for intimidating predators.

BEAK

The sharp, horny beak was perfect for gathering vegetation and cutting tough stems.

*L*ystrosaurus was a stocky, plant-eating beast that lived about 240 million years ago. Before the dinosaurs came to power, two-tusked mammal-like reptiles such as *Lystrosaurus* were the most successful animals around. Their descendants gave rise to true mammals. *Lystrosaurus* probably rooted for its food in the ancient forests and meadows, using its tortoise-like beak to slice up plants. With its large head and stout tusks, this beast was big enough to fight off most predators.

HOW BIG WAS IT?

DINO FACTS

LENGTH	70cm–1m
DIET	Probably roots and foliage of early plants such as ferns, cycads and horsetails
WEAPONS	Bulk and tusks
MEANING OF NAME	'Shovel lizard'

Lystrosaurus has been found in North America, South Africa, Russia, India, Mongolia, China and Australia. This wide range proves both the animal's success and the fact that the lands were once joined.

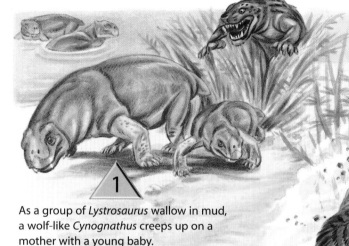

1

As a group of *Lystrosaurus* wallow in mud, a wolf-like *Cynognathus* creeps up on a mother with a young baby.

2 Desperate to protect her child, the mother *Lystrosaurus* charges at the *Cynognathus*. She knocks it over with her heavy head and tramples furiously on top of it.

3 Bruised and bloodied, the defeated predator stumbles away. The victorious mother guides her stray infant back to the safety of the group.

Did You Know?

● Given its high-set nostrils and stocky body *Lystrosaurus* was once thought by scientists to have lived an aquatic life, like a hippopotamus. Its name literally means 'shovel lizard' because it was thought it shovelled aquatic plants out of river and lake beds. But its strong, agile legs show that it was much better adapted to life on land.

● *Lystrosaurus* had powerful jaw muscles, and a lower jaw that moved backwards, forwards and from side to side, as well as up and down: ideal for grinding up tough plant food.

● In the early Triassic period when *Lystrosaurus* was alive, the continents were joined together into one great landmass known as *Pangaea*. All the land, including Antarctica, was warm and fertile. So *Lystrosaurus* could live anywhere – and it probably did.

POSTOSUCHUS

ARMOUR

The reptile's back was armoured with bony plates. This gave protection against the teeth and claws of rivals.

TAIL

The long tail balanced the body. It may have been used as a defensive lash.

BUILD

Like a crocodile, it had a thick, scaly hide and long, powerful jaws. Unlike a crocodile, though, it had long hindlegs.

SNOUT

The strong bones of the long snout would have given the beast a powerful bite.

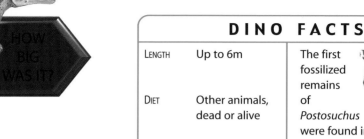

P ostosuchus was one of the most ferocious killers on our planet. This huge, well-armoured reptile had bone-crushing jaws and fearsomely sharp, serrated teeth. It was a stealthy hunter and stalked prey from dense cover, killing it with a final charge and a savage bite.

Male *Postosuchus* were probably lone hunters that competed fiercely to own the best hunting grounds and to win females with which to mate.

DINO FACTS

LENGTH	Up to 6m	The first fossilized remains of *Postosuchus* were found in Garza County, in western Texas, USA, in 1985. More remains have since turned up farther west, in Arizona. When *Postosuchus* was alive this area was part of a supercontinent known as Pangaea and was in the tropics. Much of the area was desert, but some of it was swampy and forested.
DIET	Other animals, dead or alive	
WEAPONS	Saw-like teeth for slashing open prey and carcasses	
MEANING OF NAME	'Post crocodile' (Post is a small town near where the first fossils were found)	

1 An encounter between four males leads to much baring of teeth and roaring. Some of the beasts rear up on their hindlegs to make themselves look fiercer.

Two big males start to fight. They lunge at each other, locking jaws. The fight will end only when one concedes defeat.

2

Did You Know?

● *Postosuchus* was one of the largest land carnivores of its time, second only to its close relative *Saurosuchus*, which was 7m long.

● When the first ever *Postosuchus* remains were found, the creature's bones were mixed up with those of a dinosaur – from a later period – that walked and ran on its hindlegs. Because of this, its discoverer, the fossil expert Sankar Chatterjee, wrongly believed that *Postosuchus* ran and walked on its hindlegs.

● Some scientists think that many Triassic animals such as *Postosuchus* were wiped out by the fallout from a massive asteroid impact in North America 205 million years ago – just as many experts believe that the last dinosaurs were killed off by a comet striking Earth 65 million years ago.

The Jurassic Period

Lasting for over 60 million years, the Jurassic period saw the dinosaurs become the dominant creatures on Earth. During this period, many new and extraordinary types of dinosaur emerged.

The Jurassic period was made famous by the 1993 movie *Jurassic Park*. The Jurassic age was a good choice for this film. This period saw the start of the great age of dinosaurs. Around the world, the weather was pleasant. There were large forests with ferns, huge trees and plenty of vegetation for the dinosaurs and other animals to eat. For them, Earth was a good place to live.

There were still plenty of fierce hunter-dinosaurs around, such as *Allosaurus*, an ancestor of *Tyrannosaurus rex*. Even the plant-eaters could seem ferocious. One of them, *Shunosaurus*, carried a club full of sharp spikes at the end of its tail. This was powerful enough to kill an attacker with one blow.

But as well as these meat- and plant-eaters, there were also some new types of dinosaurs with new skills. There were dinosaurs which could fly, known as pterosaurs. These included *Dimorphodon*, which flew by flapping a large piece of skin. Another flying creature was *Archaeopteryx*. This had dinosaur-type teeth, claws and tail, but it also had feathers on its arms. It was the earliest known bird.

CRYOLOPHOSAURUS

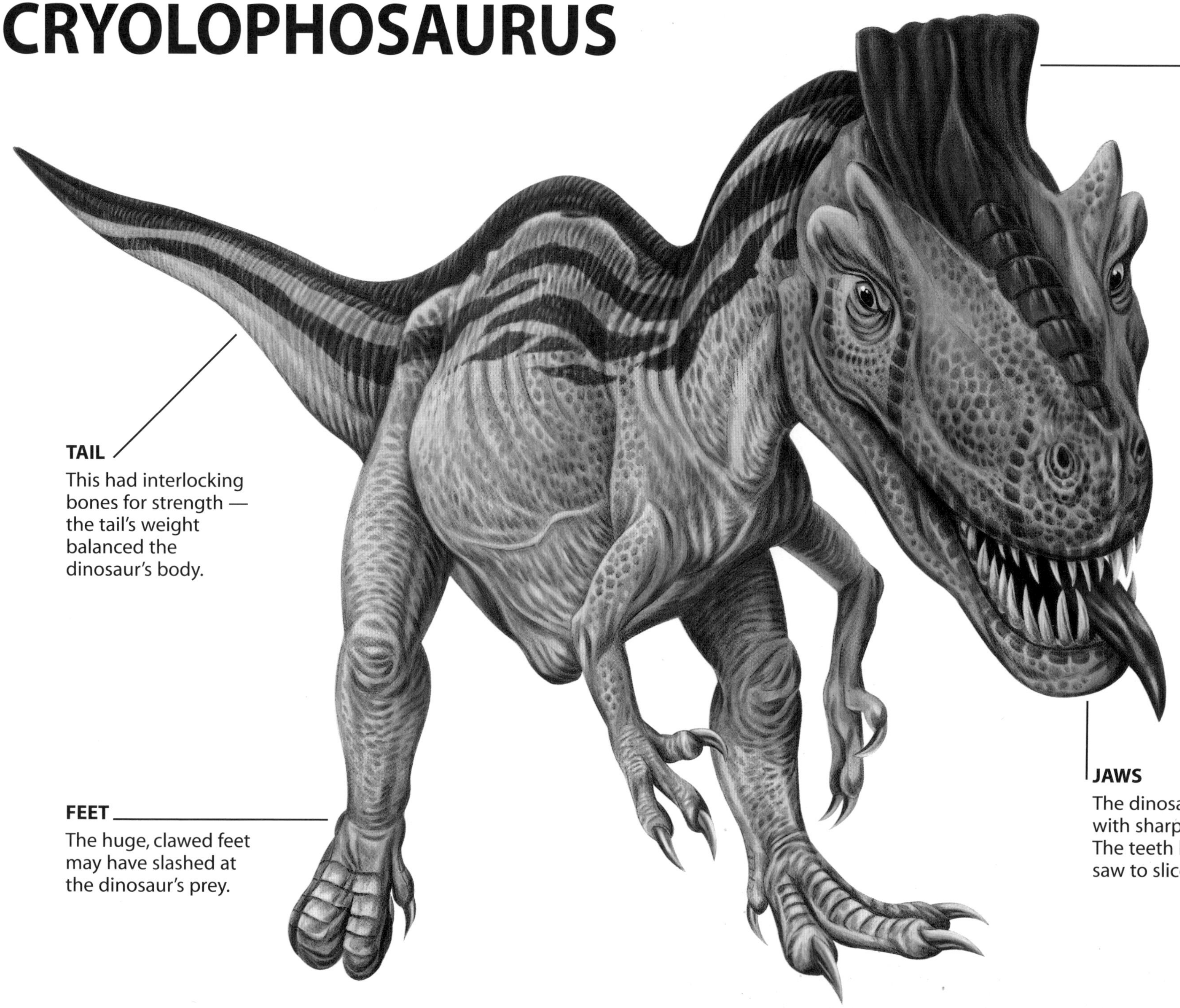

CREST & HORNS

A crest lay between two small horns. Too thin and delicate to use as a weapon, the crest may have been decoration to attract a mate.

TAIL

This had interlocking bones for strength — the tail's weight balanced the dinosaur's body.

FEET

The huge, clawed feet may have slashed at the dinosaur's prey.

JAWS

The dinosaur had massive jaws lined with sharp, backward-curved teeth. The teeth had serrated edges like a saw to slice through flesh.

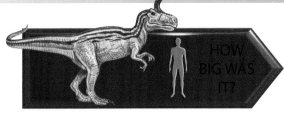

HOW BIG WAS IT?

Before Antarctica became a frozen wasteland, a ferocious predator prowled over the polar landscape. *Cryolophosaurus* was a strong, stealthy killer, although its bulky body prevented it from running fast for long. It probably hid among trees, watching a herd of plant-eaters and waiting for an opportunity to strike. When a likely victim came close, it would have made a short, high-speed chase to seize its quarry, holding it with its huge clawed limbs and biting into the victim's neck with sharp, serrated teeth.

On its head, *Cryolophosaurus* sported a bizarre crest and short horns, unlike any other prehistoric meat-eater.

DINO FACTS

LENGTH	8m or more
WEIGHT	Up to 20 tonnes
PREY	Plant-eating dinosaurs
WEAPONS	Sharp teeth and claws
MEANING OF NAME	'Frozen-crested lizard'

Cryolophosaurus was the first meat-eating dinosaur ever discovered on the ice-covered continent now known as Antarctica. This huge landmass is a frozen desert blanketed by a thick layer of ice. But at the time the killer stalked the landscape, the area was a flourishing world of plants and animals.

COLD COMFORT

Sheltering under a cliff, many *Cryolophosaurus* huddle together for warmth. In the summer, the fierce hunters fight rivals that stray into their territory. But now they need each other's warmth, and hostilities are suspended. Their plant-eating prey have to venture out to find food in the forest. When they do, the killers must gather the strength to catch a meal.

Did You Know?

● *Cryolophosaurus'* remains were found in 1991 on Mount Kirkpatrick, just 600km from the South Pole, by a US team from Augustana College, Illinois, led by Dr William Hammer.

● Before it was formally named, *Cryolophosaurus* was known as 'Elvisaurus'. Its crest reminded scientists of the hairstyle of 1950s rock-and-roll singer Elvis Presley.

● Some experts think that polar dinosaurs such as *Cryolophosaurus* were 'warm-blooded' – able to generate their own heat – like mammals do, but unlike modern reptiles, so they could survive the freezing polar winter temperatures. If they had been 'cold-blooded' they would not have been able to warm up enough to become active and hunt prey during the winter months.

DILOPHOSAURUS

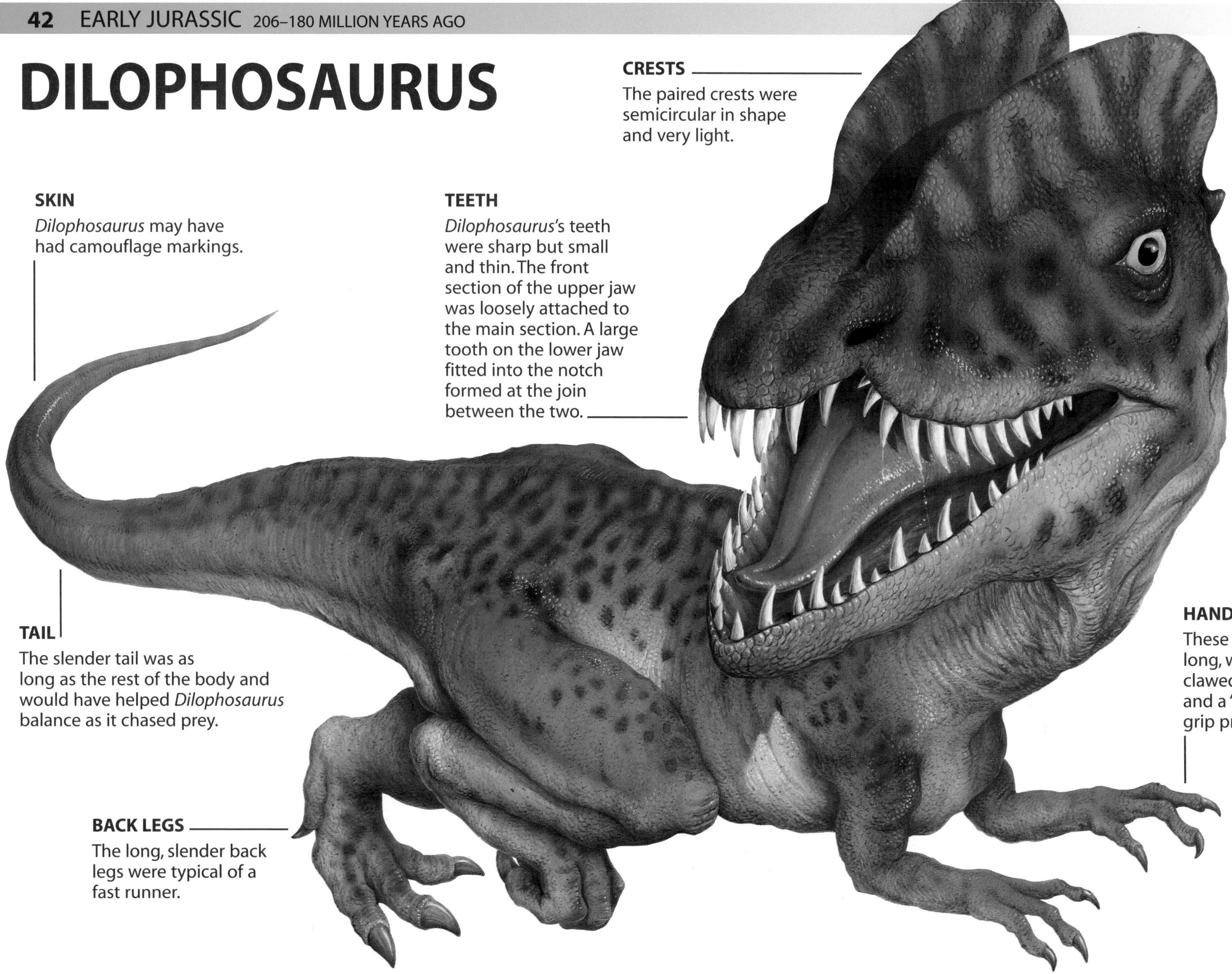

CRESTS

The paired crests were semicircular in shape and very light.

SKIN

Dilophosaurus may have had camouflage markings.

TEETH

Dilophosaurus's teeth were sharp but small and thin. The front section of the upper jaw was loosely attached to the main section. A large tooth on the lower jaw fitted into the notch formed at the join between the two.

TAIL

The slender tail was as long as the rest of the body and would have helped *Dilophosaurus* balance as it chased prey.

HANDS

These were 20cm long, with three clawed 'fingers' and a 'thumb' to grip prey firmly.

BACK LEGS

The long, slender back legs were typical of a fast runner.

This fast-moving killer with two large head crests would have sent peaceful, plant-eating dinosaurs scattering in terror as it galloped towards them. *Dilophosaurus* was slender, agile and built for speed. It could have easily outrun most dinosaurs that shared its world and, armed with sharp-clawed hands and feet, it was capable of tearing through its victim's soft flesh with ease.

Scientists are not sure why *Dilophosaurus* had the curious pair of bony head-crests on top of its head. They were far too fragile to be used in combat, but they may have been used by males when courting females or in warning displays to intimidate rivals.

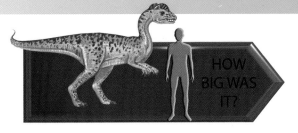

A young male is feasting on the flesh of a freshly killed plant-eater. A larger, more powerful male approaches. His bigger, brightly coloured crests show he is older and more dominant than the young male.

1

DINO FACTS

LENGTH	Up to 6m	
WEIGHT	About 450kg	
LEG LENGTH	Up to 1.5m	
PREY	Plant-eating dinosaurs, dead or alive	
WEAPONS	Needle-like teeth; sharp claws on toes and fingers	*Dilophosaurus* remains were first discovered on an expedition to a Navajo Indian reservation in Arizona in 1942. Fossils thought to belong to *Dilophosaurus* have also been found in the Yunnan region of China, in 1986, by a Kunming Museum team.
MEANING OF NAME	'Two-crested lizard'	

Did You Know?

● When fossil remains of *Dilophosaurus* were first found they were thought to belong to a species of *Megalosaurus*. It was not until a double head-crest was found with better preserved remains that *Dilophosaurus* was recognized as a different dinosaur altogether.

● A relative of *Dilophosaurus*, *Coelophysis*, was also a fast-running and savage predator. Hundreds of skeletons of this dinosaur were found at a site in New Mexico in 1947, suggesting that, like the crested *Dilophosaurus*, it too lived and hunted in packs, enabling it to bring down prey bigger than itself.

2 The newcomer thunders towards the carcass. He roars at his rival and dips his head to show the size and brightness of his superior crests. The younger dinosaur dares not risk a fight and retreats from the kill.

SCELIDOSAURUS

SKIN
Embedded in the thick, scaly skin were large, rounded nodules of bone called 'scutes'. Some of the these scutes were cone-shaped. Others looked like huge, blunt thorns.

TAIL
The tail helped to balance the dinosaur as it walked. It may have also acted as a prop when *Scelidosaurus* reared up to reach food.

HINDLEGS
The sturdy hindlegs were a little like those of a hippopotamus. Short and broad, they ended in large, flat feet with hoof-like toenails.

BEAK
The small, horn-covered beak was used to snip off leaves and small twigs. Simple teeth farther back in the jaw sliced food up.

FORELEGS
These were not quite as thick as the hindlegs, but were also built to bear the dinosaur's great weight. They were a little shorter than the hindlegs, so some scientists believe *Scelidosaurus* may have reared up to reach leaves on high branches.

Equipped with a tough, armour-plated hide, the slow-moving, plant-eating *Scelidosaurus* had little to fear. The bony knobs and spikes embedded in its skin protected it from all but the biggest meat-eaters. Any predator attempting to attack would have run the risk of seriously damaging its teeth. When cornered, *Scelidosaurus* probably squatted on all fours to protect its belly.

Scelidosaurus was the ancestor of armoured dinosaurs, although scientists are not absolutely sure who its descendants were — perhaps the mighty *Stegosaurus*, or more advanced creatures such as *Ankylosaurus*.

HOW BIG WAS IT?

Did You Know?

● A relative of *Scelidosaurus* lived in Portugal at about the same time. *Lusitanosaurus* was named after Lusitania, the old name for Portugal.

● Sir Richard Owen, who named *Scelidosaurus*, also invented the word 'dinosaur', which means 'very terrible lizard'. He came up with the word in 1842 to group the growing number of giant fossil land reptiles being described at the time.

● The *Scelidosaurus* skeleton first seen by Owen in 1863 stayed partly encased in a chunk of rock at the Natural History Museum in London until as recently as 1985.

● Scientists reckon *Scelidosaurus* probably ambled along no faster than a stately 7km/h.

1 *Scelidosaurus* was protected by bony nodules in its skin. It was a plant-eater, with simple, leaf-shaped teeth and a horny beak.

DINO FACTS

LENGTH	4m
HEIGHT	1m at the hips
WEIGHT	300kg
DIET	Low-growing plants
MEANING OF NAME	'Limb lizard'

Scelidosaurus was found in southern England. In its day, all of the world's landmasses were joined. Fossils that may also come from this animal have been dug up in the southern USA and Tibet.

2 Elephant-sized *Stegosaurus* lived tens of millions of years after *Scelidosaurus*. Huge bony back plates probably helped control its body heat. It used spikes on its tail to fend off predators. *Stegosaurus* too had a beak and leaf-shaped teeth.

3 Tank-like *Ankylosaurus* lived in the late Cretaceous. It also had bony nodules in its skin, leaf-shaped teeth and a beak. It had a heavy tail club for defence.

DIMORPHODON

WINGS

The thin skin of the wings was reinforced with thick fibres, like the spokes of an umbrella.

EYES

Dimorphodon's large eyes gave it excellent vision, like those of a bird of prey, so the hunter could spot victims at long distance.

TAIL

The long, stiff tail counterbalanced the weight of the head for greater stability in the air. The diamond-shaped skin flap on its tail probably acted as a rudder, to help steer the animal.

FINGERS

The first three fingers had gripping claws. The long fourth finger formed part of the wing.

HINDLIMBS

The powerful hindlimbs had broad, clawed toes — ideal for grabbing hold of victims.

JAWS & TEETH

Dimorphodon had big, powerful jaws lined with two types of teeth. At the front of the mouth were the long, penetrating teeth for gripping fish and other slippery creatures. At the sides there were rows of smaller, spiky teeth, probably used for slicing through the flesh of its prey.

This fearsome hunter-killer was one of the earliest pterosaurs, or flying reptiles. With its huge head, crushing jaws and vicious talons, *Dimorphodon* would have been an awesome sight as it flew on its hunting missions.

Dimorphodon patrolled the skies around 180 million years ago, feeding on aquatic and land animals. Its wings were narrow and tapered, like a swallow's, and consisted of a flap of skin attached to the forelimb and elongated fourth finger. It was capable of sustained, flapping flight and sudden plunging dives. It had good vision and, once it had a victim in its sights, there would have been little chance of escape.

Did You Know?

● As *Dimorphodon* hunted fish, it probably needed waterproof fur. Just like modern-day aquatic birds and mammals, the reptile may have had oil glands in its skin to provide a water-repellent coating. It would have preened regularly to keep its fur in good condition.

● *Dimorphodon* and other flying reptiles probably laid eggs, although no fossilized ones have been found. The female may have incubated her brood like a bird, or her eggs may have been left to hatch in a high, rocky niche that was exposed to the warming rays of the sun.

● According to experts, flying reptiles may have fed their young from throat pouches, or by bringing up partly digested food from their stomach, as many birds do today.

HOW BIG WAS IT?

A hunting *Dimorphodon* spots a lizard basking in the sun. As the eager flying reptile swoops in for the kill the startled lizard scampers for the cover of a rocky outcrop.

1

The assassin drops on to the fleeing lizard, killing the animal instantly with a snap of its jaws. The hungry hunter begins to feast on its victim, gnawing off great chunks of flesh.

2

DINO FACTS

LENGTH	2.5m, with 20cm-head, 1m-body and 1.25m-tail	The first *Dimorphodon* fossil was found in 1828 in Dorset, England, by fossil pioneer Mary Anning. Most specimens have been unearthed in south-western England, although one fossil was recently found in Mexico, proving that, at the time when the reptile was patrolling the sky, the landmasses of Europe and the Americas were part of a single continent, Pangaea.
WINGSPAN	About 1.4m	
PREY	Fish, squid and probably land animals such as lizards	
MEANING OF NAME	'Two types of teeth'	

EUSTREPTOSPONDYLUS

NECK & BACK
Powerful muscles in the animal's neck and back would have allowed the killer to twist its head vigorously to tear off great mouthfuls of flesh.

CLAWS
The dinosaur may have used these to slash at victims until they collapsed from their injuries.

SKULL
To save weight, the skull had large hollow areas, or 'windows', known as 'fenestrae'.

JAWS
The long jaws were lined with sharp, serrated teeth. Spare teeth grew constantly to replace those that were lost during an attack.

EYE RIDGES
Bony ridges protected the creature's eyes when it attacked a victim.

With its massive jaws, vicious claws and muscular legs, this dinosaur was a brutally efficient hunter, more than capable of hunting down and killing animals much larger than itself. After a rapid pursuit, the big predator would seize its victim and carve it into bite-size pieces. Scientists think it was probably a lone hunter. Even a juvenile was the size of a lion, so it could have tackled small, slow-moving plant-eaters with ease.

The only fossil skeleton yet discovered was found in sediments laid down on an ocean bottom millions of years ago. Scientists can only guess how the body of this land animal ended up at sea, where it later became fossilized.

HOW BIG WAS IT?

DINO FACTS

LENGTH	Probably 7–9m when fully grown
WEIGHT	Up to 500kg
DIET	Plant-eating dinosaurs, dead or alive
MEANING OF NAME	'Well-curved spine'

The remains of *Eustreptospondylus* were found in a clay pit just north of Oxford, in England. During the mid-Jurassic period, the Oxford area was under the sea. At this time, the earth's single landmass, known as Pangaea, was starting to break up into separate continents.

Did You Know?

● The fossil *Eustreptospondylus* was 5m long, but its vertebrae (spinal bones) appear not to be fully grown, so dino-scientists assume it was a juvenile. Adults, therefore, must have been considerably larger.

● Because the skeletal remains of *Eustreptospondylus* were found in the clay of an ancient ocean bed, some experts think the animal may have been a 'beachcomber', snapping up pterosaurs (flying reptiles) on the beach and wading into the shallows to grab fish, turtles and even sharks.

● Some scientists have suggested that *Eustreptospondylus* developed the ability to swim short distances between small islands in search of food, paddling furiously with its back legs and possibly using its tail for balance and steering.

1 On a clifftop high above a river estuary, a *Eustreptospondylus* spots a huge *Cetiosaurus*. The killer rushes at the huge plant-eater, but the cliff edge is not strong enough to support both giants.

2 As the meat-eater attacks the lumbering beast, the cliff crumbles beneath its feet, sending the predator plunging over the edge.

3 With a mighty splash, the hapless hunter hits the water. Powerful currents drag the drowning dinosaur far into the ocean. The body settles on the sea floor where it is covered by sediments and, in time, turns to stone.

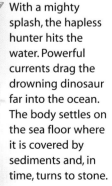

MEGALOSAURUS

HEAD
The large skull anchored the strong jaw muscles. *Megalosaurus* had quite small eyes and probably relied on smell when hunting.

TAIL
Megalosaurus may have rested on its tail and raised itself upright to look for prey.

HINDLEGS
Strong hindlegs would have enabled the beast to charge prey at speed.

JAWS
Powerful muscles would have enabled the jaws to close with tremendous force. The jaws could move sideways, giving *Megalosaurus* the leverage to shear off huge mouthfuls, which it would then have swallowed whole.

TEETH
Sharp, jagged and numerous, these were the dinosaur's primary weapons. Replacement teeth grew constantly, as the old ones broke off and fell out when biting through bone.

CLAWS
These were long, hooked and sharp for ripping through tough skin to spill a victim's blood and guts.

M*egalosaurus* lived around 170 million years ago when the landscape was filled with giant trees and thick vegetation covered the ground. This foliage provided ideal cover from which *Megalosaurus* could launch an attack on an unsuspecting victim. With jaws and teeth strong enough to tear out enormous chunks of flesh and crunch straight through to the bones, *Megalosaurus* would have been capable of killing dinosaurs much bigger than itself.

It was the first dinosaur ever described, in 1824. Until then, many people believed its fossil remains were those of a legendary giant man!

HOW BIG WAS IT?

DINO FACTS

LENGTH	About 9m	
HEIGHT	About 2m at hips	
WEIGHT	Over 1 tonne — possibly up to 4	
WEAPONS	Powerful jaws, long, pointed teeth and sharp claws	
DIET	Mainly dinosaurs, dead or alive	
MEANING OF NAME	'Great lizard'	

Megalosaurus fossil remains have been found at several sites in England, as well as at sites in Wales, France and Portugal. Other remains from as far afield as Africa and China may be those of the creature too, but experts cannot say for sure.

Prowling *Megalosaurus* follows the scent of fresh blood and finds a giant plant-eater called *Cetiosaurus*, with bleeding gashes in its legs. The predator rushes into the attack, sinking its long teeth deep into its victim's neck and tearing out a huge bite. Overcome by shock and loss of blood, *Cetiosaurus* keels over on its side – helpless to stop *Megalosaurus* eating it alive.

1

Did You Know?

● The fossil *Megalosaurus* remains described by William Buckland in 1824 were discovered by workmen, in a quarry near Oxford in England a few years earlier. The incomplete skeleton included several vertebrae and fragments of the shoulders, pelvis, jaws and hindlimbs.

● For years following Buckland's naming of the dinosaur, 'experts' referred to any partial remains of large meat-eating dinosaurs found in Jurassic or Cretaceous rocks as *Megalosaurus*! Some of these cases of mistaken identity persisted for more than 100 years, causing great confusion among dino-scientists.

SHUNOSAURUS

TAIL
As well as being used as a weapon, the long tail counterbalanced the animal's long neck.

NECK
A long neck made reaching leaves easier, but *Shunosaurus* was not big enough to reach the upper branches of the tallest trees.

BODY
The big barrel body held the large stomach and long intestine needed to digest the dinosaur's fibrous vegetable food.

HEAD
The head was tiny compared with the bulky body, but the jaws were strong enough to crop tough tree foliage.

LEGS
Strong and stout, like those of an elephant, the legs held the body well clear of the ground.

This big, long-necked plant-eater had little to fear from its enemies. It was armed with a lethal, spiked club on the end of its tail that could have sliced open an attacker with a single blow. Any predator targeting this dinosaur, or its offspring, was taking a huge risk.

Shunosaurus probably travelled in herds, browsing on horsetails, ferns and other plants of the Jurassic period. This diet was low in nutrients and slow to digest, so the *Shunosaurus* had to eat vast amounts.

Shunosaurus was an early, smaller ancestor of the giant sauropods: heavy, long-necked plant-eaters that moved about on pillar-like legs. They were the biggest animals that ever walked on land.

HOW BIG WAS IT?

DINO FACTS	
LENGTH	Up to 11m
WEIGHT	Up to 2.5 tonnes
DIET	Foliage of ferns, cycads, horsetails and conifers
DEFENCES	Spiked tail club
BREEDING	Would have laid eggs
MEANING OF NAME	'Lizard from Shu' (the old name for Sichuan Province, China, where it was found)

The fossil remains of *Shunosaurus* were found in the early 1980s in China, in the province of Sichuan, on the mountainous fringes of Tibet. In the mid-Jurassic period, when *Shunosaurus* was alive, there was just one huge landmass, called Pangaea, which was starting to break up into separate continents.

1 A hungry *Megalosaurus* spots a young *Shunosaurus* that has wandered away from its mother. Breaking from cover, it charges at the helpless infant. But its attack run alerts the adult, who lashes out at the hunter with her spiked tail club.

The mighty *Megalosaurus* is left stunned and disoriented, and makes a hasty escape. The irate parent directs an ear-splitting bellow at her enemy's back. The youngster has had a nasty fright and now huddles nervously under its mother for protection.

2

Did You Know?

● More than 20 nearly complete skeletons of *Shunosaurus* have been found in China. This makes it one of the best studied of all the sauropods.

● The tail club was missing from the first *Shunosaurus* finds. As the experts did not know about the tail club, they put the fossil on display without it. This is still how the beast is shown in many books today.

● Some experts think sauropods flicked their tails like a whip, both to make a noise, so they could 'talk' to other members of their herd, and for defence. This would have made *Shunosaurus'* tail club even deadlier.

ALLOSAURUS

BACKBONE
The name *Allosaurus* means 'strange lizard' – a reference to the unique design of its backbones.

TAIL
Allosaurus was very top-heavy. Without its massive tail to act as a counterbalance, it would have fallen flat on its face.

TEETH
Each jaw bristled with 30 or more teeth. New teeth grew to replace ones lost during violent struggles to subdue prey.

SKULL
Allosaurus had a bony bump above each eye, and a bony ridge from the forehead to the tip of the snout. The purpose of this headgear is not known, but it may have been a mark of rank among the dinosaurs.

LEGS
The dinosaur's powerful legs, the size of tree trunks, were able to launch its five-tonne weight towards prey at high speed.

CLAWS
The 'hands' of *Allosaurus* each bore three razor-sharp claws, not two as in *Tyrannosaurus rex*. They were capable of cutting through the flesh of its victims.

The 'great-grandfather' of *Tyrannosaurus rex*, this incredibly powerful animal was also a frighteningly efficent killing machine, spreading terror wherever it went. *Allosaurus* would seize prey with its muscular front limbs, inflicting terrible wounds with its razor-sharp claws. Sabre-like fangs lined its jaws, which could tear off and swallow huge chunks of flesh with ease.

Allosaurus was an abundant and widespread as well as bloodthirsty beast. The largest and most ferocious killer on land in the Jurassic age, its reign of terror lasted for at least 15 million years, from around 150–135 million years ago.

HOW BIG WAS IT?

DINO FACTS

LENGTH	Up to 12m	
WEIGHT	Up to 5 tonnes	
HEIGHT	Up to 5m	
TEETH	5–10cm	
CLAWS	Up to 15cm	
PREY	Other dinosaurs; also scavenged carcasses	
MEANING OF NAME	'Strange lizard'	

Allosaurus ranged far and wide. Thousands of its bones, plus well-preserved footprints, have been discovered in North America. Farther afield, scientists have dug up skeletons in Portugal, Tanzania and Australia.

1

Allosaurus probably relied on its superb sense of smell to locate prey. Fossil skulls have been found with nostril openings that are as large as a human hand. At much closer range, it would have used sight and hearing to home in on a target.

Did You Know?

● There are four similar species of *Allosaurus*. *Allosaurus fragilis* was the first to be discovered, in 1877. The other species are *A. amplexus*, *A. atrox* and *A. ferox*.

● Recent studies suggest that, unlike the reptiles living today, large meat-eating dinosaurs such as *Allosaurus* could regulate their body temperature – like modern mammals and birds do, although not as efficiently.

● One quarry in Utah, USA, has produced more than 40 *Allosaurus* skeletons, ranging in size from full-grown adults to 3m-long youngsters.

2

Leaping out from behind cover to pounce on a victim, *Allosaurus* may have stunned or even killed its prey with the force of its initial impact. It grasped larger victims in its powerful front limbs, letting it deliver crunching bites to the neck and backbone. It would then have used its serrated teeth to saw off great lumps of flesh.

After dining on one of its favourite meals, here a *Camptosaurus*, it may have rested for several days, before hunger forced it to seek its next victim.

APATOSAURUS

TAIL
The tip would have cracked like gunshot when *Apatosaurus* lashed its whippy tail.

SPINE
Rope-like ligaments reinforced the spine, supporting it from head to tail-tip.

BODY
The body contained the vast fermentation tank of the belly, where bacteria helped digest the vegetation eaten each day.

FEET
Huge, flat-soled feet spread the load. Some fossilized sauropod footprints, found today in rocks, can hold almost 300 litres of water!

TEETH
Peg-like teeth raked foliage, and chisel-like teeth snipped stems. Each tooth was replaced as soon as it wore out.

*A*patosaurus was one of the sauropods — enormous, long-necked, long-tailed, plant-eating dinosaurs. It needed to eat around a tonne of spiky leaves every day and probably munched for most of its waking hours.

Fossils reveal that this giant-sized dinosaur had legs like tree trunks and a body the size of four or five African elephants. But, despite its huge size, *Apatosaurus* still had to watch out for predators, such as *Allosaurus*, fighting them off with whiplash blows from its powerful tail.

HOW BIG WAS IT?

DINO FACTS

LENGTH	Up to 21m	
WEIGHT	30 tonnes	
HEIGHT	4.5m at shoulder; up to 12m standing	
FOOT SIZE	1m long	The first *Apatosaurus* fossils were found in the Morrison Formation. This is a vast, layered 'sandwich' of river and lake deposits in North America, stretching south from Montana through Wyoming, Utah and Colorado.
FOOD	Vegetation, particularly palm foliage and conifer needles and cones	
MEANING OF NAME	'False lizard' or 'trick lizard'	

A long neck gave *Apatosaurus* access to a good supply of food: treetop foliage. Some scientists reckon it reared up on its hindlegs to reach leafy crowns.

1

2

At the front of its jaws, *Apatosaurus* had two rows of peg-like teeth with chisel edges for chopping up stems. It had no chewing teeth, so it gulped down rough mouthfuls, relying on its stomach acids, bacteria and the grinding action of stones in its belly to break the food down.

Did You Know?

● Fossil tracks in Texas show that *Apatosaurus* probably travelled in herds, with adults on the outside protecting young on the inside.

● An adult *Apatosaurus* may have had up to 45kg of big stones in its metre-wide gizzard (foregut) to grind up the plant food that it ate.

● Othniel Marsh was one of the scientists studying American fossil finds in the late 19th century. He named *Apatosaurus* in 1877 and *Brontosaurus* in 1879, not realizing that his later 'discovery' was also based on *Apatosaurus* bones. The name *Brontosaurus* is not used today.

ARCHAEOPTERYX

WINGS
Long forelimbs supported the wings. However, some scientists doubt that the wrist joint was loose enough to allow powered flight.

FEATHERS
The structure of the feathers was very like that of modern birds.

FEET
Three toes pointing forwards and one pointing backwards provided a perching grip. No dinosaur had this feature – it is exclusive to birds.

CLAWS
Archaeopteryx had three claws on each wing. This bird used its claws to climb trees.

TEETH
Lined with sharp, pointed teeth, the jaws were like those of other meat-eating dinosaurs.

TAIL
Modern birds have no tail bones, but *Archaeopteryx* had a long, bony tail more typical of a reptile.

*A*rchaeopteryx is the earliest known bird, found in fossils from the late Jurassic period, 150 million years ago. It had the teeth, claws and tail of a killer dinosaur – and the plumage of a bird. It probably lived in open forest, gliding between trees on its feathered arms. *Archaeopteryx* was about the size of a pigeon, but its mix of features suggests that it could be a halfway stage in the evolution of birds from reptiles. Its remains hold clues to the evolution of flight in birds, but no one knows for sure how flight started.

HOW BIG IS IT?

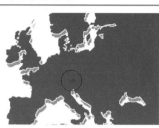

DINO FACTS	
LENGTH	35cm
WEIGHT	Estimated 300–400g
DIET	Insects and small lizards
MEANING OF NAME	'Ancient wing from the printing stone' (its fossils were found in limestone used for making prints)

All specimens of *Archaeopteryx* discovered to date have been found in the limestone deposits of Bavaria, southern Germany. The bird certainly lived elsewhere, but its fragile remains have been found only in rocks with a very fine grain.

Perhaps *Archaeopteryx* took to clambering in trees, to find new food sources and avoid ground-living predators. After a few test launches into the air, it could have developed the ability to glide – then to fly.

1

2 Alternatively, it set out from the ground. Cautious flaps helped it to jump ever higher – and, finally, to develop powered flight.

Did You Know?

● So far, eight *Archaeopteryx* fossils have been found: a single feather and seven skeletons.

● The *Archaeopteryx* fossils are of such high quality that they have been rejected by some people as fakes. But microscopic study has proved they are all genuine.

● One *Archaeopteryx* fossil, dug up in 1958, stayed in the possession of its finder – Eduard Opitsch – until his death in 1992. Its whereabouts today are a complete mystery.

● Two feathered dinosaurs were found in China in 1998. They are not birds, as they lack a rear-facing big toe. *Caudipteryx* and *Protoarchaeopteryx* are, in fact, meat-eating dinosaurs.

BRACHIOSAURUS

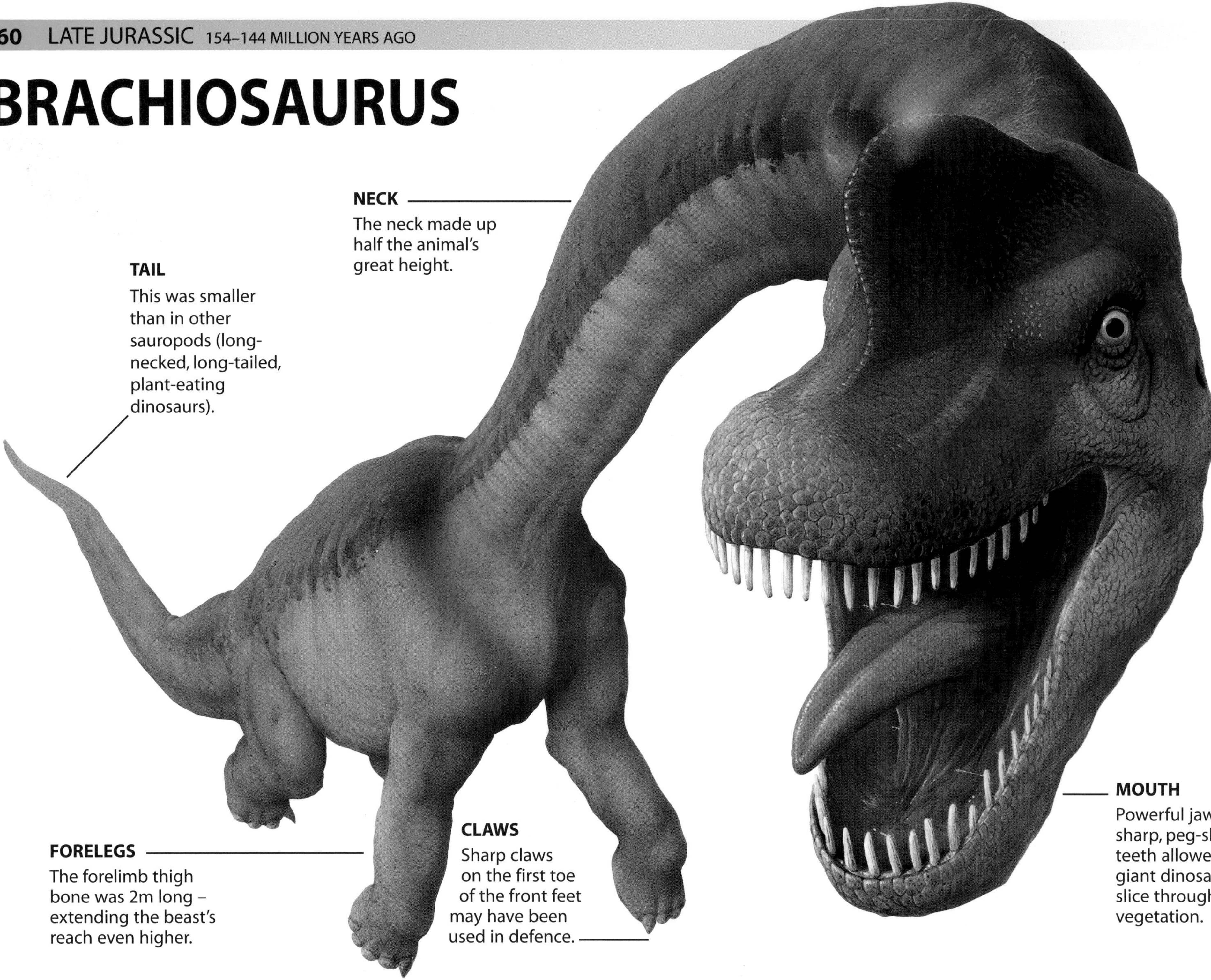

NECK

The neck made up half the animal's great height.

TAIL

This was smaller than in other sauropods (long-necked, long-tailed, plant-eating dinosaurs).

FORELEGS

The forelimb thigh bone was 2m long – extending the beast's reach even higher.

CLAWS

Sharp claws on the first toe of the front feet may have been used in defence.

MOUTH

Powerful jaws with sharp, peg-shaped teeth allowed the giant dinosaur to slice through tough vegetation.

The ground would have shaken as *Brachiosaurus* lumbered through the prehistoric forests. This dinosaur was as heavy as 12 fully grown African elephants, and its immense size made it a daunting opponent for potential enemies. Its hugely long neck allowed it to reach as high as a three-storey building to browse on the tree-tops. It needed a huge amount of food each day just to stay alive. If there were leaves it could not reach it would simply push the tree over to get at them.

Brachiosaurus may also have used its long, versatile neck as a weapon in ritual battles for dominance between rival males.

HOW BIG WAS IT?

Raising its head up high, an adult *Brachiosaurus* feeds on the tenderest leaves of a tall conifer. In the background, two males spar for the right to lead the herd and mate with the females.

1

DINO FACTS

LENGTH	Over 23m from nose to tail
WEIGHT	50–80 tonnes
REACH	14m above the ground
DIET	Conifers, palms and ferns
MEANING OF NAME	'Arm lizard'

Brachiosaurus lived on a land mass called Gondwanaland. This super continent has since broken up, which explains why *Brachiosaurus* fossils have been found in Colorado and Utah in the USA, and also in Tanzania, Algeria and Portugal.

2 The long neck may also have been useful for feeding on the forest floor – probing into narrow spaces between trees to find vegetation. A youngster, safe in the shadow of its massive mother, follows her lead and munches contentedly on the softest plants.

Did You Know?

● There is evidence of dinosaurs even larger than *Brachiosaurus*. One, named *Ultrasauros*, is known from a single leg. The size of this suggests the animal was 27m long.

● Some fossil-hunters think *Brachiosaurus* used its tail like a giant whip to knock down predators.

● *Brachiosaurus* probably lived in family herds of up to 20.

● The weather in the Jurassic was warm and wet all the time, creating ideal growing conditions for the vegetation on which *Brachiosaurus* fed.

● *Brachiosaurus* takes its name 'arm lizard' from its long forelegs.

● Experts think dinos like *Brachiosaurus* lived up to 100 years.

CERATOSAURUS

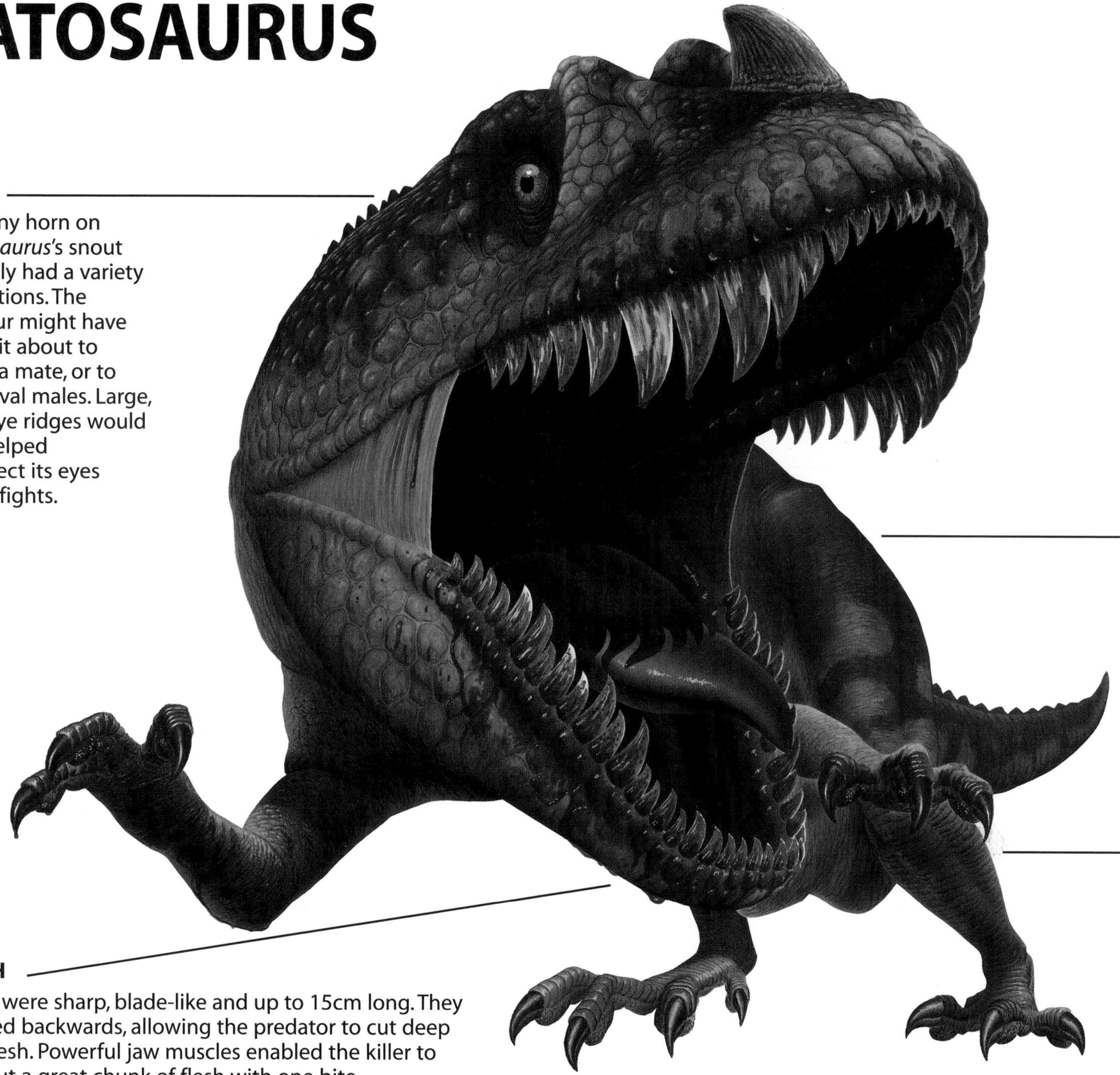

HEAD

The bony horn on *Ceratosaurus*'s snout probably had a variety of functions. The dinosaur might have waved it about to attract a mate, or to deter rival males. Large, bony eye ridges would have helped to protect its eyes during fights.

BACK

A high arch to the back made *Ceratosaurus* look bigger than it really was. A line of bony plates running along its spine added to the deception. Some experts think that the most important function of these plates was to radiate heat and so cool the animal down in hot weather.

TEETH

These were sharp, blade-like and up to 15cm long. They pointed backwards, allowing the predator to cut deep into flesh. Powerful jaw muscles enabled the killer to tear out a great chunk of flesh with one bite.

HINDLEGS

Ceratosaurus was a bipedal (two-legged) carnivore that moved around on its hindlegs. The legs would have provided a rapid burst of speed when it set off after fast-moving prey.

Ceratosaurus was a striking-looking dinosaur with a bony horn on its snout, ridges of bone over its eyes and dragon-like plates down its back. Its powerful jaws, long fangs and slashing claws mark it out as one of the top killers of the Jurassic period.

An agile hunter, *Ceratosaurus* was fast enough to catch swift-running animals, but it may also have ambushed prey from behind cover, battering them with its horned head. It was also fierce enough to chase other hunters away from their kills.

DINO FACTS

LENGTH	4.5–6m	
HEIGHT	2m at hip; 3m at head	
WEIGHT	Over 1 tonne	
DIET	Probably plant-eating dinosaurs; may have scavenged carrion	
MEANING OF NAME	'Horned lizard'	
LIFESPAN	Unknown	

Five *Ceratosaurus* fossils have been unearthed in quarries in the Rocky Mountains of Utah and Colorado, in the USA. Other fossil finds, thought to be *Ceratosaurus*, have been made in Tanzania, East Africa.

1

Speed and ferocity were essential if *Ceratosaurus* was to overcome a heavily armoured plant-eater such as a two-tonne *Stegosaurus*. The mighty defender's long, lashing tail had lethal spikes that could inflict heavy damage.

2

Ceratosaurus charges the slow-witted target, ramming its horned head into the animal's side and tearing at the prey's flesh with its sharp teeth and claws. Bleeding heavily, *Stegosaurus* lashes out with its tail, but the killer is already out of harm's way. Now weak from loss of blood, the victim slumps to the ground, and the victor moves in for the kill.

Did You Know?

● *Ceratosaurus* remains were first found in 1884, at a Colorado quarry. Fossil hunters found an almost complete skeleton, plus other partial ones. The dinosaur was studied by Othniel Charles Marsh, a leading dino-expert of the time, and it was he who gave it its name.

● Most experts think *Ceratosaurus* was a solitary predator that tackled mainly medium-sized plant-eaters. However, a trail comprising several sets of fossilized *Ceratosaurus* footprints casts doubt on this long-held theory. As a pack hunter, *Ceratosaurus* would have been able to attack and kill much larger prey.

COMPSOGNATHUS

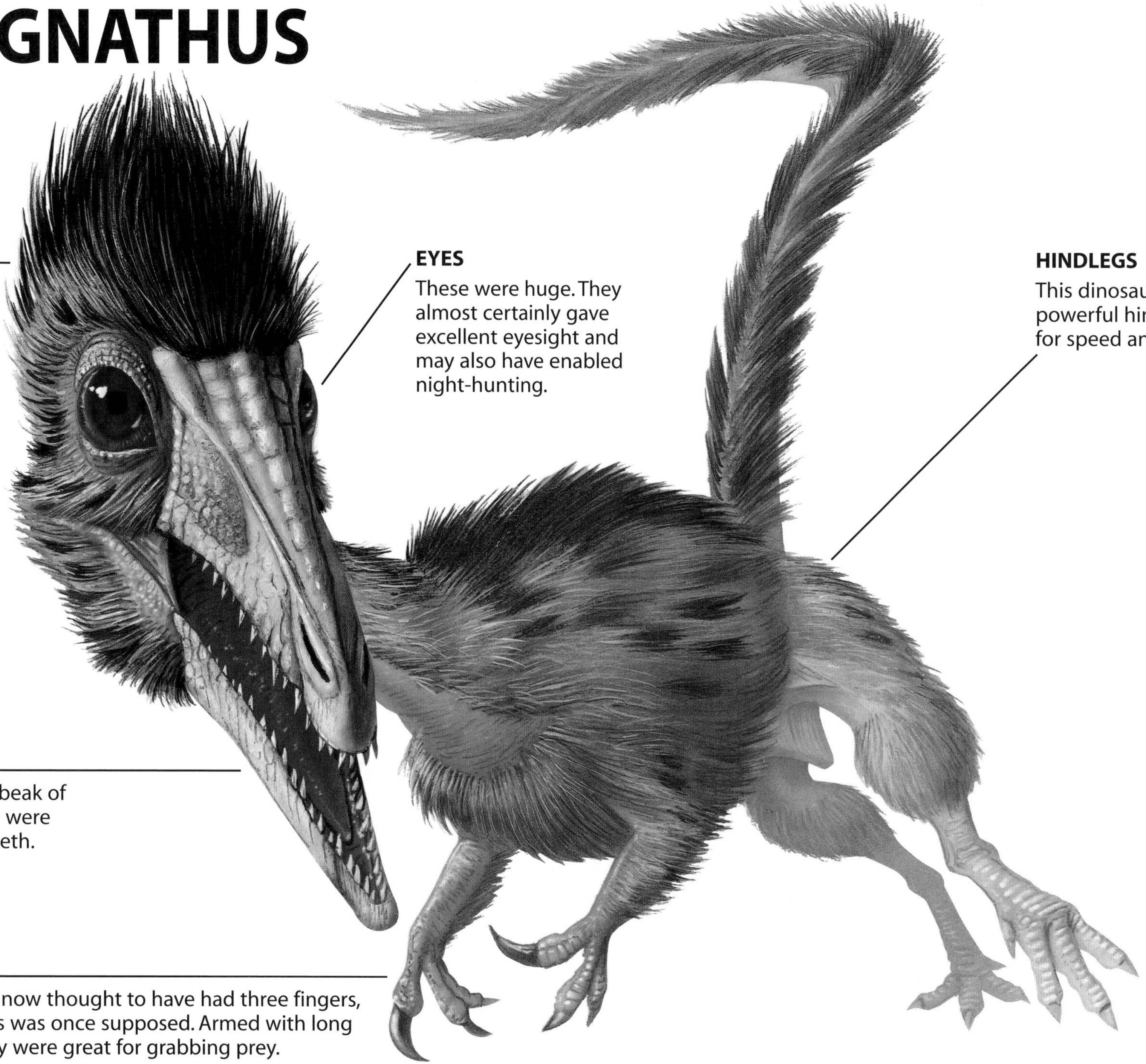

PLUMAGE

Many scientists believe there was a bristly coat all over the body. It would have kept the animal warm at night. It may also have made *Compsognathus* more attractive to potential mates or more intimidating to its enemies.

EYES

These were huge. They almost certainly gave excellent eyesight and may also have enabled night-hunting.

HINDLEGS

This dinosaur had powerful hindlegs, for speed and agility.

TEETH

Lining the bird-like beak of the *Compsognathus* were sharp saw-edged teeth.

HANDS

These are now thought to have had three fingers, not two as was once supposed. Armed with long claws, they were great for grabbing prey.

Despite the fact that *Compsognathus* was the smallest dinosaur of them all, a lizard or an early shrew-like animal would have had to run like the wind to escape its snapping jaws. This small, fierce dinosaur had powerful hindlegs for speed and agility, incredibly good eyesight and a bird-like beak.

All the *Compsognathus* fossils found so far lay near the shorelines of ancient lakes and shallow seas. In what is now Europe, the dinosaur lived on small islands with scrubby vegetation. The remains of this bird-like creature have helped scientists to form new ideas about the link between modern birds and their ancient ancestors, the dinosaurs.

HOW BIG WAS IT?

Did You Know?

● By coincidence, the two main fossil specimens of *Compsognathus* had the tail broken in exactly the same place.

● Some scientists claim they have found eggs inside the body cavity of a *Compsognathus* fossil. The bumps were once thought to be remains of skin. No one is sure whose idea is right – especially as the skeleton was first identified as a young dinosaur.

● The fine detail preserved in the *Compsognathus* fossils is due partly to the fact that, when the animals died, their bodies sank to the oxygen-free conditions at lake beds. This prevented the rapid process of decay, helping the bones to turn into rock.

● The European rocks that yielded *Compsognathus* also contain fossil pterodactyls (flying reptiles).

DINO FACTS

LENGTH	70cm to 1m	
WEIGHT	3–3.5kg — roughly the size of a chicken or turkey	
DIET	Lizards, mammals and probably insects	
MEANING OF NAME	'Delicate jaw'	

Compsognathus fossils have been found at Canjuer in Var, southern France, and at Solnhofen in Bavaria, southern Germany. Related animals include *Sinosauropteryx* from China, *Aristosuchus* from Britain, and unnamed remains from Brazil and Portugal.

1 Scientists once thought *Compsognathus* paddled between islands in search of food, dipping its head to snap up aquatic prey. They based this idea on a fossil that seemed to have flipper-like limbs. In fact, the 'flippers' were fossilized wood!

2 Today, we are sure this small, agile dinosaur lived on land. Here it scampers along a sandy bay, about to pounce on a tiny Jurassic lizard.

KENTROSAURUS

PLATES

The horny plates may have been covered with skin, helping the beast to warm itself up in the sun.

BACK

Scientists think *Kentrosaurus* fed mainly on small plants. Its body sloped steeply from the hips, lowering its head closer to its food.

SPIKES

The bony back plates grew longer and spikier towards the tail. This made a highly effective weapon.

HINDLEGS

These were twice as long as the forelegs, enabling *Kentrosaurus* to rear up to reach food.

HEAD

Kentrosaurus had an amazingly tiny skull and an even tinier brain. A toothless beak was good for stripping leaves.

TOES

Heavy, hoof-like claws helped support the dinosaur's weight as it plodded about in search of food.

This huge, shambling, plant-eating dinosaur roamed Africa around 150 million years ago, chomping on plant after plant. But what *Kentrosaurus* lacked in speed and agility it made up for with its vicious spikes, which could have inflicted terrible wounds on its enemies.

Bony plates along the dinosaur's back were probably arranged in two upright rows. Scientists believe that they may have been used to absorb the sun's heat to help *Kentrosaurus* warm up after a cold night. Towards the tail, the plates became larger and narrower, forming pairs of lethal spikes covered with tough horn.

Did You Know?

● Although *Kentrosaurus* weighed almost two tonnes, it had a brain the size of a prune. Despite this, the area of the brain connected with smell was relatively big, so the beast probably had a sensitive nose.

● *Kentrosaurus* had small, weak teeth, so experts think it swallowed stones to grind up plant food in its stomach – just like crocodiles today.

● If *Kentrosaurus* had skin-covered plates, they may have flushed red to advertise its availability in the mating season or as a warning to predators.

● Between 1909 and 1913, a team from the Berlin Natural History Museum found over 225 tonnes of fossils of many different dinosaurs in Tendaguru.

HOW BIG WAS IT?

With its bulky body and lumbering gait, *Kentrosaurus* would have seemed a relatively easy target for predators – but they soon learned that its viciously spiked tail was not just for show.

1

DINO FACTS

LENGTH	Up to 5.5m	
WEIGHT	Up to 2 tonnes	
DIET	Mainly low-growing plants	
DEFENCES	Spikes	
MEANING OF NAME	'Spiked lizard'	

Fossils of *Kentrosaurus* have been found only in the area of Tendaguru in Tanzania, East Africa. A German engineer discovered the first bones in 1907 as he was searching for gemstones, at a time when Tanzania was a German colony. His find led to a major dino-hunt in the area two years later.

2 A young female *Allosaurus* tries to sneak up on an adult male *Kentrosaurus*. He soon picks up her scent and bellows in warning. Foolishly, she edges closer. With a violent lunge he drives a spine deep into her neck.

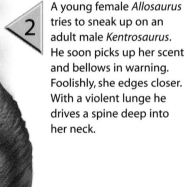

ORNITHOLESTES

EYE
Big eye sockets suggest that *Ornitholestes* would have hunted as much by sight as scent.

NECK
Slender and flexible, this allowed the head to move in all directions to snap up quick-moving creatures.

FINGERS
Ornitholestes probably caught small prey in its clawed hands, gripping them with its long fingers.

CREST
Some scientists think that *Ornitholestes* had a small bony crest on its nose, like a stumpy rhinocerous horn.

TEETH
The sharp, pointed teeth could grip small, struggling prey.

Sleek, fast and agile, *Ornitholestes* was a predatory dinosaur that once roamed the forests of North America. It had strong arms, grasping hands and long claws — ideal for grabbing victims and tearing off flesh. *Ornitholestes* probably specialized in dashing after swift-moving prey. Its long hindlegs allowed it to sprint like a greyhound and, balanced by its whip-like tail, it was amazingly agile. It could leap, twist and pounce to outmanoeuvre its victims. It may also have formed into packs with other of its kind to hunt and kill larger plant-eating dinosaurs.

DINO FACTS

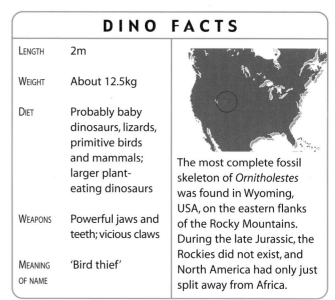

LENGTH	2m
WEIGHT	About 12.5kg
DIET	Probably baby dinosaurs, lizards, primitive birds and mammals; larger plant-eating dinosaurs
WEAPONS	Powerful jaws and teeth; vicious claws
MEANING OF NAME	'Bird thief'

The most complete fossil skeleton of *Ornitholestes* was found in Wyoming, USA, on the eastern flanks of the Rocky Mountains. During the late Jurassic, the Rockies did not exist, and North America had only just split away from Africa.

1 A drought drags on, and food is scarce. Three baby *Ornitholestes* squeal with hunger as their mother appears with a juicy lizard.

HOW BIG WAS IT?

2 As meat becomes scarcer, the babies grow thin and weak, then finally die. The adults are almost starved themselves, so gobble up their dead offspring before abandoning the nest for good.

Did You Know?

● *Ornitholestes* was discovered in 1900 by Henry Fairfield Osborn at Bone Cabin Quarry, where dinosaur fossils are so common a shepherd had once used some to build a hut!

● *Ornitholestes* was given the name 'bird thief' because Osborn imagined it hunted *Archaeopteryx*, a primitive form of bird. Yet there is no evidence to suggest that the two animals lived in the same area, or even on the same continent.

● The few fossils of *Ornitholestes* found might suggest it was rare. More likely, its slender bones were usually gobbled up by scavengers.

OPHTHALMOSAURUS

DORSAL FIN
The triangular dorsal fin was a fleshy extension rather than a true bony fin like that in a fish.

BUILD
The creature had a powerful build designed to slip through the water with ease. It was streamlined from snout to tail.

TAIL
Deep and curved, this beat from side to side to propel the animal along at high speed.

FLIPPERS
All four limbs were modified to form paddles for tight steering and quick 'braking'.

TEETH
The long jaws were full of conical teeth for grasping wriggling prey.

This ancient fish-like reptile had huge eyes the size of grapefruit, which gave it fantastic vision – ideal for chasing swift and slippery fish in prehistoric seas.

Ophthalmosaurus was built for speed and endurance. Its sleek fins, streamlined body and massive tail allowed it to power through the water looking for fish or squid to snatch up in its long, teeth-filled jaws.

Marvellously intact fossil remains show that *Ophthalmosaurus* and other ichthyosaurs (marine reptiles) gave birth to live young underwater, much like modern-day whales and dolphins. Some fossils are females with unborn babies inside; others are females who died while giving birth.

Did You Know?

● *Ophthalmosaurus* had more 'toes' in its broad flippers than most of its relatives. ichthyosaurs normally had five digits in each flipper, but this reptile had no fewer than eight.

● When ichthyosaur fossils were first discovered in England in the early 18th century, most people thought that they were the remains of extinct dolphins or crocodiles that were wiped out in the great flood of Noah's Ark fame.

● The largest ichthyosaur ever unearthed – in Nevada in the USA – was an enormous beast known as *Shonisaurus*, which grew to 15m long. This early ichthyosaur lived more than 200 million years ago, in the late Triassic. It had a long, tapering tail and a pair of huge paddle-like flippers, each up to 2m long.

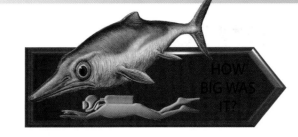

HOW BIG WAS IT?

A pregnant *Ophthalmosaurus* drifts through the sea, her body trembling with convulsions as she tries to expel her baby. But there is a problem with the birth, and she is steadily weakening from blood loss.

1

DINO FACTS

LENGTH	3–4m
WEIGHT	Probably up to 500kg
EYES	10cm wide
PREY	Mainly squid and fish
MEANING OF NAME	'Eye lizard'

Fossilized *Ophthalmosaurus* remains – many of them complete – have been found at sites as far afield as northern Europe and North and South America: in England, France, Canada, the USA and Argentina.

2 The female has barely enough strength to rise to the surface for a final gasp of air before she succumbs to exhaustion. Inevitably, as her lifeless body drifts down, the baby trapped in her birth canal perishes too.

3 Long after coming to rest on the seabed, mother and baby are no more than skeletons sinking into the silt to become fossils.

SEISMOSAURUS

HEAD
Many experts believe that *Seismosaurus'* head was no bigger than that of a large horse.

TAIL
The tail helped to stabilize the animal as it moved. It may also have supported the beast as it reared up on its hindlegs to browse tall trees.

TEETH
The teeth are thought to have been like long pegs. They were used for raking pine needles from the branches of tall conifers.

LEGS
The pillar-like legs ended in huge, flat feet. These were ideal for spreading the dinosaur's immense weight, but made it a slow mover.

NECK
The huge neck enabled *Seismosaurus* to reach 15m up into the trees.

Seismosaurus is the largest animal with a backbone ever known – half as long again as a blue whale. Two of these giants standing end to end would have stretched the length of a football pitch. More than half its length was made up by its tail, which had to be long to counterbalance its huge, heavy neck when it walked.

Despite its size, Seismosaurus was a peaceful plant-eating dinosaur. It would have had few enemies – its massive size made it difficult to attack. But some scientists believe that it may have defended itself from groups of predators with its whip-like tail.

HOW BIG WAS IT?

DINO FACTS

LENGTH	An estimated 45m
HEIGHT	15m at head, 5m at hip
WEIGHT	Up to 100 tonnes
DIET	Leaves
MEANING OF NAME	'Earthshaker lizard'

Only one Seismosaurus skeleton has been unearthed so far. It was found in 1979, in the Ojito Wilderness Study Area, 60 miles north-west of Albuquerque in New Mexico, USA. Until more remains are discovered, the animal's full range cannot be estimated.

Did You Know?

● The only Seismosaurus found so far has been nicknamed 'Sam' by dino-scientists. Some experts think Sam may have died as a result of a huge gastrolith (stone) getting stuck in its throat or gut. One of the gastroliths uncovered with the remains was the size of a grapefruit – much bigger than any of the others discovered.

● The tooth of a killer dinosaur was found with the Seismosaurus bones. This might mean the dinosaur was killed by a predator, but the tooth was more likely lost when the meat-eater scavenged the carcass.

● Not all scientists believe that Seismosaurus fed from treetops. Some argue that it would have had difficulty lifting its head higher than its shoulders.

1 Riddled with disease, a full-grown Seismosaurus collapses and dies as it is crossing a mighty river. The fast-moving water carries the great body to a sandbank, where it becomes stuck. Soon, scavenging flying reptiles are at work, tearing strips of meat from the beast's body.

2 The gut is ripped open and the insides spill on to the sand. More meat-eaters appear to tear at its flesh. The remaining tissue rots off, leaving behind the skeleton.

3 Some bones wash away and the rest are buried by sand. Dissolved minerals soak into the bones, preserving them for millions of years. Finally, the wind and rain expose the bones to the air – and the eyes of fossil hunters.

STEGOSAURUS

BODY
Estimated at 6-7m in length and weighing around 2 tonnes, this was a real monster of a dinosaur.

BACK PLATES
Two walls of intimidating bony plates ran along its back from head to tail. Scientists are still unsure of their function.

HEAD & JAWS
The head was tiny in relation to the body. A toothless beak at the front of jaws contained small, weak cheek teeth.

TAIL
The tail bristled with two pairs of pointed spikes. It could have been a lethal weapon, like the deadly maces swung by medieval knights in jousting tournaments.

FORELEGS
The sturdy, long-thighed legs end in flat feet, tipped with rounded claws. They were like those of an elephant and are similarly built for carrying the dinosaur's weight, rather than for speed.

This plant-eater had a secret weapon when it came to fending off enemies – a swishing tail armed with strong spikes. With a body the size of a truck, *Stegosaurus* was the largest of all the stegosaurs, a group of dinosaurs that thrived for 70 million years.

Stegosaurus had a wall of big, bony plates on its back that ran from its head to its tail. Scientists are not sure what the plates were used for, but they may have helped the animal keep its body temperature stable. The plates were probably laced with blood vessels and, when angled towards the sun, could absorb heat rapidly.

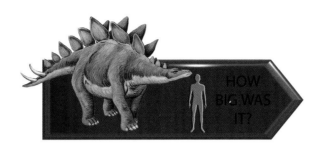

HOW BIG WAS IT?

DINO FACTS

LENGTH	Up to 9m, average 6–7m	
WEIGHT	Up to 2 tonnes	
DIET	Soft vegetation	Fossils of *Stegosaurus* have been found in what are now the states of Colorado, Oklahoma, Utah and Wyoming, USA. They were laid down in the Morrison Formation, a vast slice of sedimentary rock in the Midwest. The Morrison has yielded thousands of dinosaur bones over the last century or so.
PLATES	60cm tall on the back	
MEANING OF NAME	'Roofed lizard'	

1 Still dozy after a bulky meal of leaves, a *Stegosaurus* is surprised to find a young *Allosaurus* thundering towards it. Slow *Stegosaurus* has no chance of running away. It must stand and fight.

2 As *Allosaurus* leaps in with claws flailing, *Stegosaurus* lashes out with its tail. The spikes catch the killer off-guard.

Did You Know?

● About 3cm long, the brain of *Stegosaurus* probably weighed no more than one-thousandth of the animal's total body weight.

● The fossil remains of other stegosaurs were discovered in the 1960s in northern Siberia – inside the Arctic Circle, where today the temperatures are freezing for much of the year. However, the stegosaurs probably did not catch a chill: millions of years ago, Arctic temperatures were mild.

● Scientists used to believe that the plates of *Stegosaurus* lay flat upon its back, overlapping one another like tiles on a roof.

● Other stegosaur fossils have been discovered in China, southern India and western Europe.

3 A spike has stabbed *Allosaurus*'s leg. The deep wound may become infected and stop the dinosaur from hunting. It could even result in sickness and death.

The Early Cretaceous Period

Lasting from around 146 to 127 million years ago, the early Cretaceous period saw the development of the first flowering plants. With this new vegetation came new types of dinosaurs.

During this period of the Earth's history, plants with seeds first developed. This meant there was plenty of lush vegetation for plant-eating dinosaurs such as *Iguanadon*. This big dinosaur had special grinding teeth and a long gut to help digest plant matter – but it also had huge thumb spikes to defend itself again predators.

Some of the largest carnivores (meat-eaters) that ever lived were around in the early Cretaceous. The *Acrocanthosaurus* was around 12 metres long, and the *Giganotosaurus* measured a massive 14 metres in length, making it the largest meat-eating dinosaur ever. Some plant-eating dinosaurs 'grew' their own protection against these huge killers. *Amargasaurus*, for instance, grew bony spikes down its back to stop attackers biting it. Another dinosaur, *Hypsilophodon* developed huge eyes so that it could spot danger coming, and hide from the big hunters.

The rivers and seas of the early Cretaceous period were full of marine creatures to feed dinosaurs. One Cretaceous dinosaur, *Baryonyx*, even had a big claw on each thumb to spear fish.

ACROCANTHOSAURUS

SPINES

The spines were up to 45cm high. These may have been for used defence, but some experts think they were part of a 'sail' used to control temperature.

EYES

The large eyes would have been able to spot prey at a distance. The eyes were topped by hard 'eyebrow bumps', which probably gave some protection from the claws of other killers.

TAIL

Like other two-legged dinosaurs, this animal held its long tail out for balance while running.

NOSE

Acrocanthosaurus had a highly developed sense of smell. It would have been able to track victims by scent.

CLAWS

The 'fingers' and toes ended in vicious, hooked claws. Its 'hands' could rip at the flesh or grip an animal firmly while the powerful legs and feet got to work.

TEETH

The hunter's jaws contained 68 thin, blade-like teeth. These were used for ripping at the flesh of prey.

The mighty *Acrocanthosaurus* once roamed the North American plains. One of the biggest meat-eaters of its day, *Acrocanthosaurus* could have tackled even gigantic plant-eaters. Its huge, razor-sharp teeth and long claws were made for swift and ruthless killing.

Footprints discovered in the USA show that the dinosaur hunted like a tiger does today. It speeded up to its prey, then lunged at its victim, slashing it to death with its teeth.

HOW BIG WAS IT?

DINO FACTS

LENGTH	9–12m	At its height, this predator probably roamed across a coastal plain that once extended across the USA from Texas to Maryland. Remains of *Acrocanthosaurus* have been found in Oklahoma, Texas and Utah in mid-western and central-southern North America.
HEIGHT	About 4m at head	
SKULL	1.4m	
WEIGHT	2 tonnes or more	
PREY	Plant-eating dinosaurs	
METHOD OF ATTACK	Multiple bites to kill by shock and blood loss	
MEANING OF NAME	'High-spined lizard from Atoka County'	

1 A male *Acrocanthosaurus* is eager to breed, but the big female could eat him for breakfast. He tries to win her approval by dropping a piece of meat at her feet.

The blood-drenched flesh smells delicious to the hungry female. The gift pays off, and they mate. But next time it could be the male that ends up as the female's meal.

2

Did You Know?

● Tooth marks in the skeleton found in Oklahoma may have been made by another *Acrocanthosaurus*, suggesting there was fierce rivalry between individuals of the species.

● The longest known skull of any meat-eating dinosaur is a 1.8m *Giganotosaurus* skull. The African *Carcharodontosaurus* had a 1.6m skull, *Tyrannosaurus rex*'s head was 1.5m long and *Acrocanthosaurus*' skull was 1.4m.

● When prey was scarce or hard to catch, *Acrocanthosaurus* probably scavenged the carcasses of old kills, as mammalian predators such as lions and leopards do today.

AMARGASAURUS

SKIN COLOUR

No one knows for sure, but some experts think that the skin colour would have helped to camouflage the creature.

TAIL

Held out straight, the long tail would have counterbalanced the long neck.

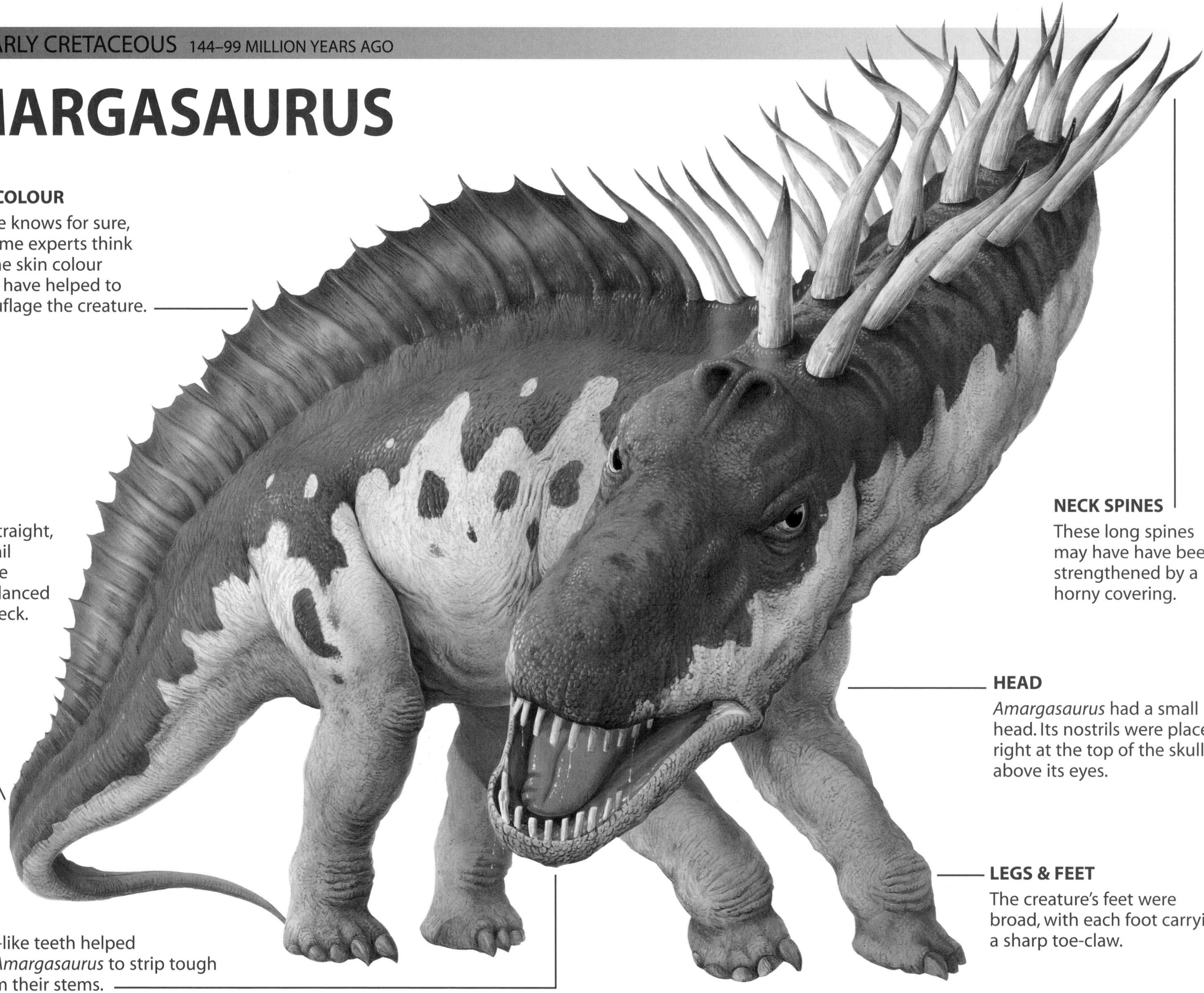

TEETH

Blunt, peg-like teeth helped a hungry *Amargasaurus* to strip tough leaves from their stems.

NECK SPINES

These long spines may have have been strengthened by a horny covering.

HEAD

Amargasaurus had a small head. Its nostrils were placed right at the top of the skull, above its eyes.

LEGS & FEET

The creature's feet were broad, with each foot carrying a sharp toe-claw.

One of the strangest dinosaurs ever discovered, *Amargasaurus* had an intriguing mane of bony spikes all the way down its neck and back. The double row of neck spikes would have made this dinosaur a hard target for hungry predators. Some experts think that the spikes on its back may have been covered with skin to make an impressive display sail.

Twice as long as an African elephant, this prickly plant-eater once roamed the plains of Argentina.

HOW BIG WAS IT?

DINO FACTS

LENGTH	About 10m	Fossils of *Amargasaurus* were discovered in the La Amarga canyon area of Argentina by Guillermo Rougier, a student of the famous Argentine dino-expert José Bonaparte. The skeleton he found was almost complete – only the front of the skull and part of the tail were missing. The dinosaur was named *Amargasaurus* by Bonaparte and his colleagues in 1991.
HEIGHT	About 2m at hip	
DEFENCES	Large size and possibly horny sheathed spikes	
WEIGHT	About 5 tonnes	
DIET	Large amounts of plants such as conifers, gingkoes, ferns and cycads	
MEANING OF NAME	'Lizard from La Amarga'	

1

A herd of *Amargasaurus* is grazing contentedly. But its peace is suddenly shattered when a huge, sharp-toothed *Giganotosaurus* thunders towards the group.

2

The terrified animals move away as fast as they can. One of the youngsters runs under the belly of an adult, protected by its great legs. But the other can not keep up. It is easy for the mighty predator to snap up the little dinosaur in its terrible jaws.

Did You Know?

● There were several different families of sauropods – the huge, long-necked, plant-eating dinosaurs. *Amargasaurus* belonged to the diplodocid family, all of which were surprisingly light for their size. This was because their vertebrae (backbones) were partly hollow and so weighed less than if they had been made of solid bone.

● An African dinosaur called *Dicraeosaurus*, another member of the diplodocid family, also had huge forked spines sticking up from its spine. But this dinosaur lived a long time before *Amargasaurus*, in the late Jurassic period.

BARYONYX

NOSTRILS
These opened on top
of the flat snout.

CREST
The Baryonyx had
an odd little crest
on top of the head,
almost between
the eyes.

SKIN
We can not tell for
sure if the skin was
scaly or smooth.

THUMB
A huge claw on the
first finger of each
hand probably served
as fishing tool and as
a weapon.

TEETH
The sharp,
conical teeth
were ideal for
catching slippery
prey. The lower
jaw had 32 teeth
on each side,
twice the
number in most
meat-eating
dinosaurs.

JAWBONE
Long and slender, this
made an S-bend like that
of a modern crocodile.

The chance find of a huge claw led to one of the greatest dinosaur discoveries of the 20th century – the fossil skeleton of a truly weird meat-eating dinosaur. Its mighty thumb-claws earned it the nickname 'Claws' when its remains were found in 1983.

Scientists believe that *Baryonyx* was a top-class catcher of fish. Half-digested fossil scales of ancient fish were found close to its remains. It may have used its mighty thumb-claws to hook fish from the ancient rivers. *Baryonyx* had a long, narrow snout, like that of a crocodile, so it may have used its sharp teeth to snap fish from the water.

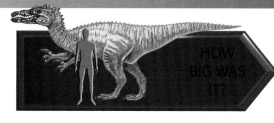

HOW BIG WAS IT?

CATCH OF THE DAY

Plodding on its hindlegs through an ancient river, *Baryonyx* peers into the water in search of prey. Seeing a shoal of fish, the dinosaur lashes out with its huge thumb-claws. Eventually it lifts a thumb-claw from the water, dripping with blood and bearing the first struggling catch of the day.

Baryonyx almost certainly used its mouth too. With a swift snap of those toothy jaws it could have plucked a mouthful of fish from the rapids.

DINO FACTS

LENGTH	9m
HEIGHT	2.5m to the hips
WEIGHT	2–3 tonnes
SIZE OF HAND CLAW	28cm core; would have been even longer when sheathed in horn
PREY	Fish, other dinosaurs
MEANING OF NAME	'Walker's heavy claw', in honour of William Walker, who found the first claw

Fossil remains of *Baryonyx* were found in southern England in the Wealden Clay rock formation (marked in red). Possible remains from Spain and Africa have yet to be verified.

Did You Know?

● *Baryonyx* might have been warm-blooded and quite capable of an energetic, drawn-out pursuit after prey on land.

● In *Baryonyx* 's day, southern England was not the mild, leafy land that it is today. Western Europe was then a tropical flood plain cloaked in swampy, steamy forests. Plants such as horsetails, cycads, ferns and conifers grew in abundance.

● Dinosaur scientists Angela Milner and Alan Charig, of the British Museum of Natural History, London, officially named *Baryonyx* in November 1986.

CARCHARODONTOSAURUS

SKULL
The skull's beak-like shape may have been used for reaching into rotting carcasses.

TEETH
Rows of grooves on the teeth helped the dinosaur hold on to a slippery meal.

CLAWS
Powerful claws could hold prey down while the jaws went to work.

TAIL
Scientists think that the dinosaur held its tail aloft while it ran, to counterbalance its large head.

BODY
Estimated at up to 13.5m long, mighty *Carcharodontosaurus* was even larger than *Tyrannosaurus rex*.

One of the most ferocious carnivores ever to roam our planet, this huge dinosaur had huge, jagged teeth that sliced through its victims' flesh with ease. It was larger than three family-sized cars and weighed more than a hundred fully grown people. Its immense size was a huge advantage against other dinosaurs.

A predator as large as this dinosaur needed plenty of meat. As well as stalking and killing prey, it probably also fed on any dead creatures it came across.

Some experts think that the massive dinosaurs may have cared for their young as birds do today.

HOW BIG WAS IT?

While their mother is away hunting, three baby *Carcharodontosaurus* hide quietly in a patch of ferns. When they hear her return they all rush out into the open and beg noisily.

DINO FACTS

LENGTH	Up to 13.5m	Scattered teeth and pieces of bone belonging to *Carcharodontosaurus* were discovered in northern Africa in the 1920s, but it was not until 1995 that pieces of an almost complete fossilized *Carcharodontosaurus* skull were found, in the Sahara Desert, in the Kem Kem region of Morocco.
WEIGHT	Up to 8 tonnes	
SKULL	1.6m long	
WEAPONS	Immensely powerful jaws, 12.5cm-long teeth and sharp claws	
DIET	Other dinosaurs, dead or alive, and fish	
MEANING OF NAME	'Shark-toothed lizard'	

Did You Know?

● *Carcharodontosaurus'* skull shows that the mighty creature's brain was only half the size of that of *Tyrannosaurus rex* and only about one-eighth the size of a human brain.

● The team that discovered the skull of *Carcharodontosaurus* also found a new dinosaur named *Deltadromeus*, which means 'delta runner', on the same expedition.

● Another massive predatory dinosaur, *Giganotosaurus*, found in Argentina, is thought by most experts to be a close relative of *Carcharodontosaurus*. They think the two beasts may have evolved from a common ancestor.

Their mother has swallowed chunks of prey. She spits them on to the ground for her babies, just as a bird spits up insects for its chicks. The lumps of meat are partly digested, so easier for her young to eat.

DEINONYCHUS

HEAD

The big head was relatively light because of openings in its skull, known as *fenestrae*. Large eye sockets suggest that the beast had good eyesight.

TEETH

The teeth would have sliced through flesh with ease. The teeth often broke off during an attack, but new ones grew in their place.

SICKLE CLAW

This was hinged like a flick knife. It had a bony core with a horny covering.

FORELIMBS

These were quite long, allowing *Deinonychus* to reach forwards and swipe.

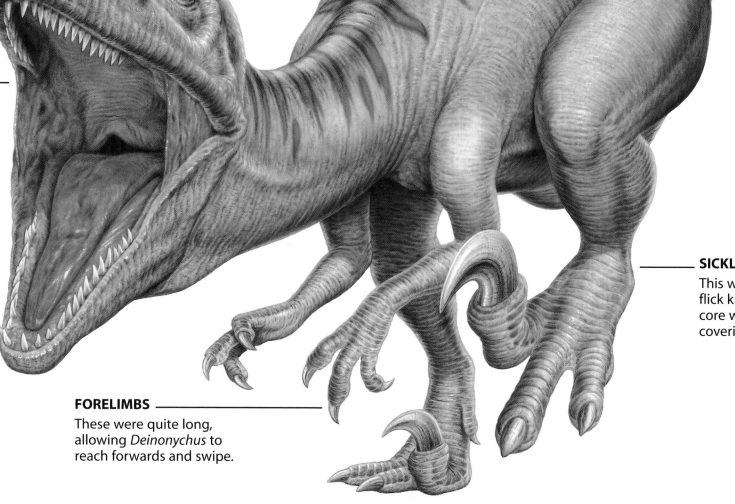

Equipped with rows of saw-edged teeth and viciously curved claws, this killer dinosaur was one of the most brutally efficient hunters of its time. *Deinonychus* probably hunted in packs to track and attack much bigger prey. Its savage weapons could have inflicted horrific wounds on its victims.

Deinonychus' remains were discovered in 1964 by fossil expert John Ostrom. At that time, most scientists believed that dinosaurs were lumbering, pea-brained hulks. Ostrom said that the large skull and muscular legs of *Deinonychus* proved that the creature was an intelligent and agile killer.

HOW BIG WAS IT?

DINO FACTS

LENGTH	3–3.3m
HEIGHT	Nearly 1.8m
WEIGHT	70–75kg
DIET	Probably plant-eating dinosaurs, alive or dead
WEAPONS	Sharp, curved, saw-edged teeth; foreclaws and vicious sickle-shaped hindclaws
MEANING OF NAME	'Terrible claw'

Deinonychus bones have been unearthed in the US states of Wyoming, Oklahoma, Montana, Utah and Maryland. John Ostrom was the first to describe its remains, in the 1960s, but not the first to discover its bones. Barnum Brown found *Deinonychus* fossils in the 1930s – but never got around to naming it.

Four *Deinonychus* are tracking a lone *Iguanodon*. Choosing their moment, they race to surround it. As the killers leap on to the quarry, they deliver slashing kicks with their sickle claws.

1

2 Bellowing in pain, the victim topples over. As it falls it crushes one of the attackers under its great bulk.

3 The killers begin to devour the big plant-eater, even before it has drawn its last breath. Another pack of *Deinonychus* arrives, and the two groups fight to claim the steaming carcass.

Did You Know?

● *Deinonychus* was closely related to *Velociraptor*, the savage dinosaur seen in the film *Jurassic Park* (1993). In real life, *Velociraptor* was only 1.8m long, including its tail. The predators in the film were actually modelled on *Deinonychus*; however neither beast lived in the Jurassic period.

● Scientists reckon that an adult *Deinonychus*, lashing out with its vicious sickle claw, would have left a lethal 1m-long wound in its victim.

● In some parts of Wyoming and Montana, more than 40 per cent of *Tenontosaurus* fossil finds include a scattering of *Deinonychus* teeth.

GIGANOTOSAURUS

TAIL
The long tail helped to counterbalance *Giganotosaurus* as it moved. It was probably held out straight behind the dinosaur.

SKULL
The massive skull was long and narrow. It had several large holes, or *fenestrae*, to reduce the weight. Bony ridges around the eyes would have reduced the animal's forward vision.

NOSTRILS
Large nostrils and a good sense of smell would have helped the animal find living prey and dinosaur carcasses.

FORELIMBS
Giganotosaurus' tiny arms were almost useless. Their only functions might have been to help the dinosaur get off the ground or grip a partner during mating.

TEETH
The teeth were slender, like daggers, with serrated edges – ideal for carving through flesh.

Giganotosaurus was the largest meat-eating dinosaur that ever hunted on land. It was bigger even than the mighty *Tyrannosaurus rex*. With its scissor-like jaws and jagged teeth, it could have bitten through flesh like a knife slicing through butter. Its jaws were large enough to swallow an adult human whole! As if its size did not make it terrifying enough, *Giganotosaurus* may have hunted in packs to bring down enormous plant-eating dinosaurs.

HOW BIG WAS IT?

DINO FACTS

LENGTH	14m	*Giganotosaurus* may have ranged widely over South America, but so far its fossil remains have been found only near the Patagonian towns of El Chocon and Plaza Huincul in Argentina. Today, Patagonia is dry and wind-swept, but during the mid-Cretaceous period it was humid and lush with plants – perfect for the plant-eaters that *Giganotosaurus* must have lived on.
HEIGHT	4.5m at hip; 7m at head	
WEIGHT	Up to 8 tonnes	
DIET	Other dinosaurs	
MEANING OF NAME	'Giant lizard of the south'	

Spotting a baby *Argentinosaurus* that has strayed from the herd, *Giganotosaurus* dashes in and kills it with a single bite to the neck. The herd look on helplessly as the killer begins its meal.

1

On another occasion, the smell of a dead dinosaur draws the big meat-eater to the carcass. After chasing away smaller scavengers, it tucks in.

2

Did You Know?

● *Giganotosaurus* is only one of several amazing dinosaurs found in South America in recent years. Others include the huge plant-eater *Argentinosaurus*, the strangely horned hunter *Carnotaurus* – and a massive killer, unearthed in 1999, that may turn out to have been even bigger than *Giganotosaurus*.

● A multiple-fossil discovery in Canada suggests that *Tyrannosaurus rex* may have hunted in packs, just as *Giganotosaurus* may have done.

● *Giganotosaurus* is believed to be closely related to another giant predator, *Carcharodontosaurus*, which lived at the same time in what is now Africa. Scientists believe this shows there were land connections between Africa and South America in the mid-Cretaceous period.

HYPSILOPHODON

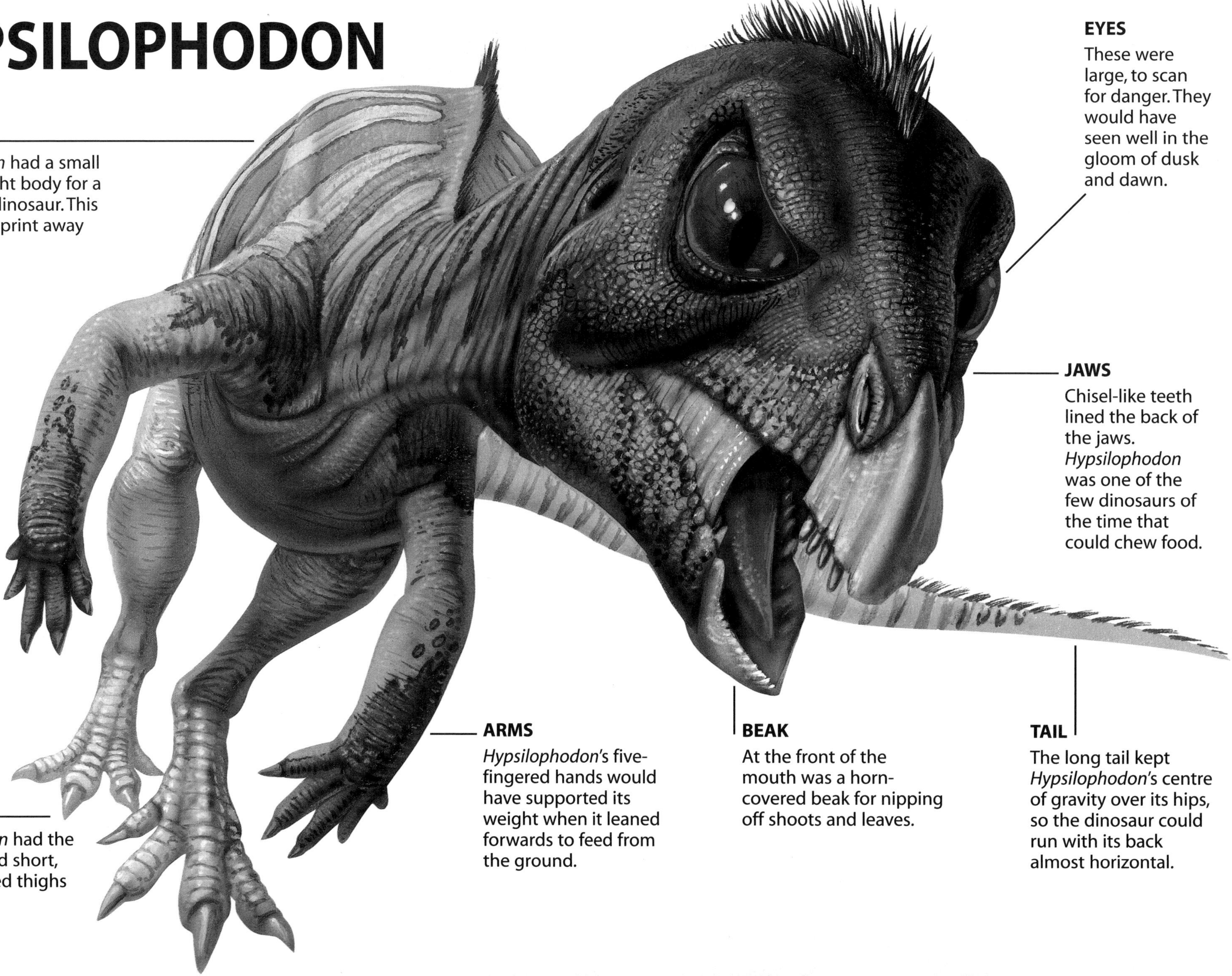

EYES

These were large, to scan for danger. They would have seen well in the gloom of dusk and dawn.

BODY

Hypsilophodon had a small and lightweight body for a plant-eating dinosaur. This allowed it to sprint away from trouble.

JAWS

Chisel-like teeth lined the back of the jaws. *Hypsilophodon* was one of the few dinosaurs of the time that could chew food.

ARMS

Hypsilophodon's five-fingered hands would have supported its weight when it leaned forwards to feed from the ground.

BEAK

At the front of the mouth was a horn-covered beak for nipping off shoots and leaves.

TAIL

The long tail kept *Hypsilophodon's* centre of gravity over its hips, so the dinosaur could run with its back almost horizontal.

LEGS

Hypsilophodon had the long shins and short, muscle-packed thighs of a sprinter.

Not all plant-eating dinosaurs were big and slow. *Hypsilophodon* was so small and athletic it could outrun most of its enemies. It was one of the first dinosaurs identified and is known from almost perfectly preserved specimens. More than 20 skeletons were found lying close together on the Isle of Wight in southern England, which suggests that these animals lived in herds. It is not known how they died, but they were probably killed by a flash flood or drowned in quicksand.

HOW BIG WAS IT?

1 *Baryonyx* bursts from some trees to attack a *Hypsilophodon* herd. But it is spotted instantly.

The little plant-eaters scatter. They are too fast and agile for the huge meat-eater, which soon gives up the chase.

2

DINO FACTS

LENGTH	2m
HEIGHT	70cm at hip; 80cm at head
WEIGHT	Estimated at 50kg
DIET	Low-growing plants
MEANING OF NAME	'High-ridged tooth'

Hypsilophodon remains have been found in England, Spain and South Dakota in the USA. As more fossils are found in the future, its actual range may prove to have been even larger.

Did You Know?

● When *Hypsilophodon* was first discovered, experts mistakenly thought it was a young *Iguanodon*. It was only 20 years later that the eminent scientist Thomas Huxley realized it was a new dinosaur.

● The *Hypsilophodon* fossils found in England, Spain and the USA were probably different species, for sea split Europe and the Americas 125 million years ago. As with all one-word dinosaur names, the name *Hypsilophodon* refers to the genus, a group of closely related species.

● *Hypsilophodon* had relatives right around the globe. Dinosaurs of the family Hypsilophodontidae have been unearthed on every continent. They include *Atlascopcosaurus*, *Fulgurotherium* and *Leaellynasaura*, which were all found in Australia.

IGUANODON

JAWS

The sharp, toothless beak was used for nipping of tasty twigs and leaves.

BODY

The body was large, with a huge stomach and long gut. This was needed to digest tough plant matter.

TEETH

Iguanodon ground up plant matter with the molars in the back of its jaws. When they broke, replacements grew up from underneath.

TAIL

The long, heavy tail made a useful balance when *Iguanodon* walked on two legs. It was also used as a prop when the dinosaur reached into high branches for food.

HANDS

Five-fingered hands doubled as forefeet when the beast walked on all fours. The thumb was a big spike, probably used for defence.

Many meat-eating dinosaurs would have liked to make a meal of *Iguanodon*. But with huge thumb spikes to defend itself, this big plant-eater was no easy conquest. This highly successful dinosaur had a horny beak, a specialized set of grinding teeth, and a long gut to aid digestion. It was the first animal of its size to have such advanced eating apparatus, and it soon outnumbered more primitive plant-eaters.

One of the first dinosaurs to be discovered, *Iguanodon* was named before the word 'dinosaur' was even invented. During its time on Earth, *Iguanodon* spread across the planet — a success proven by widespread fossil remains.

HOW BIG WAS IT?

DINO FACTS

LENGTH	10m
HEIGHT	3m at hip; 5m at head
WEIGHT	4.5 tonnes
DIET	Plants
MEANING OF NAME	'Iguana tooth'

Iguanodon fossils have been found in Europe, Mongolia, North America and Africa. In its day, the landmasses lay in different places (they have drifted since), so *Iguanodon* was able to spread far and wide.

1 Early in the morning, before it has time to warm up in the sun, *Iguanodon* is still very slow. An early-rising *Spinosaurus* takes advantage of its sleepiness to attack.

2 Taken completely by surprise, *Iguanodon* flails its forelimbs. A thumb spike strikes lucky, gouging its attacker's right eye. The *Spinosaurus* is driven off, half blinded by the big spike.

Did You Know?

● Two of the 39 *Iguanodon* specimens dug up at Bernissart, Belgium, had had arthritis in their ankles. Where the bones of the feet met those of the lower leg, they were so deformed that the ends looked like flattened mushrooms.

● Two species of *Iguanodon* have already been described and named. The smaller of the two, *Iguanodon atherfieldensis*, was only 7m long. A third species has recently been discovered in North America, and a fourth has been found in Mongolia.

KRONOSAURUS

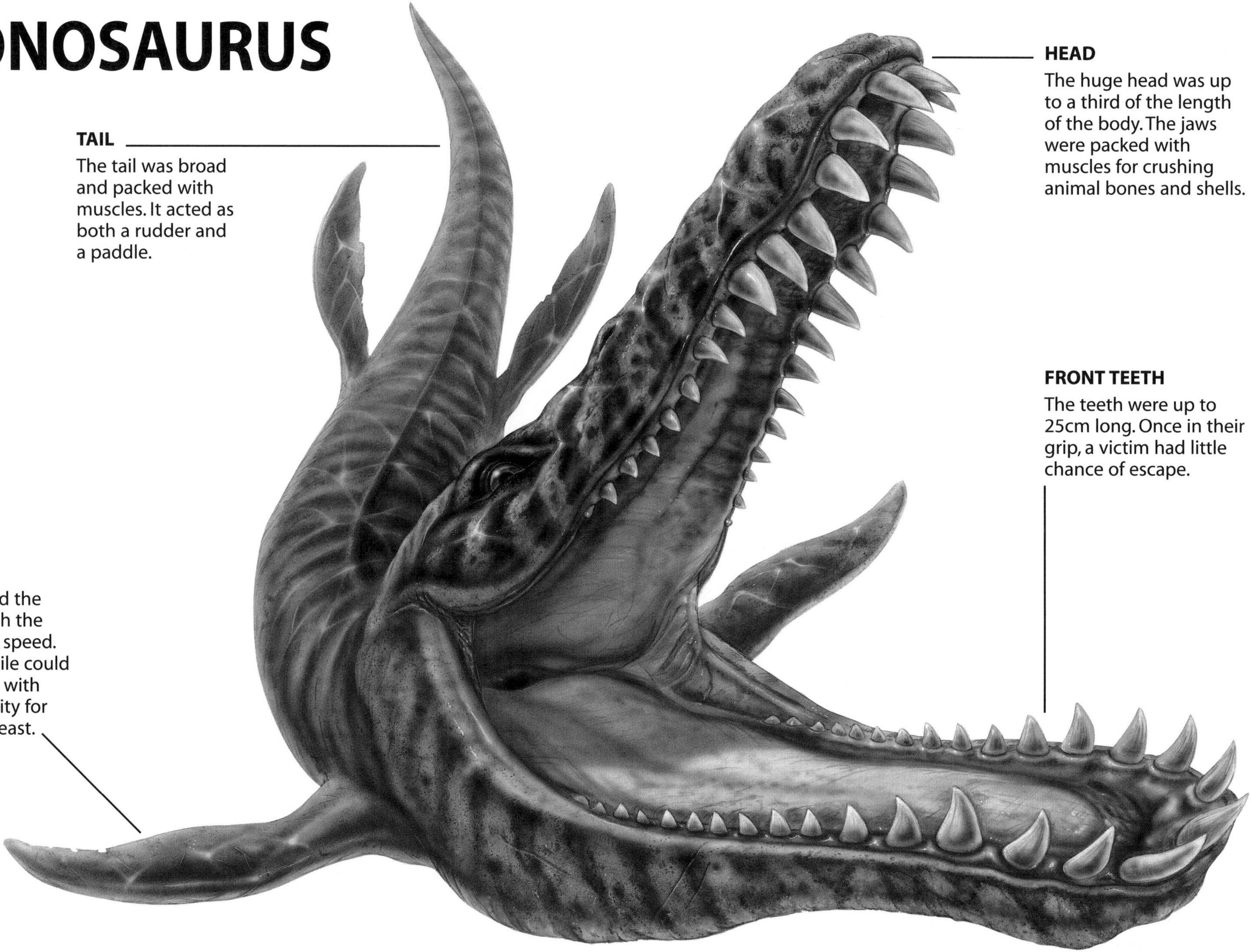

HEAD

The huge head was up to a third of the length of the body. The jaws were packed with muscles for crushing animal bones and shells.

TAIL

The tail was broad and packed with muscles. It acted as both a rudder and a paddle.

FRONT TEETH

The teeth were up to 25cm long. Once in their grip, a victim had little chance of escape.

FLIPPERS

These powered the animal through the water at great speed. The great reptile could twist and turn with surprising agility for such a large beast.

The ancient seas swarmed with huge reptiles snapping at anything that moved. One of the scariest was the mighty *Kronosaurus*. This gigantic reptile terrorized the oceans. Its massive skull held huge jaws packed with terrifying teeth – essential weapons for butchering large reptiles and fish. Fossil remains can tell us what *Kronosaurus* looked like, but we do not know whether it came ashore to lay eggs or gave birth to live young in the water.

HOW BIG WAS IT?

DINO FACTS

LENGTH	Probably 7–9m	
WEIGHT	Possibly up to 20 tonnes	
PREY	Fish, molluscs and reptiles of all sizes, such as sharks, turtles and plesiosaurs	Fossilized *Kronosaurus* remains, first found in 1899, are known only from sites in the state of Queensland, Australia. They are remains of animals that swam in a shallow inland sea. However, fossils found in Colombia in South America in 1992 may also be of the beast.
MEANING OF NAME	'Titan lizard'	

1 Some scientists think the female *Kronosaurus* dragged herself up a beach to lay her eggs. Perhaps she buried them in the sand like turtles do today.

Did You Know?

● The most famous *Kronosaurus* skeleton, at Harvard University in the USA, has jokingly been called *Plasterosaurus* by some scientists, who query the amount of plaster of Paris used in its reconstruction.

● In Greek mythology, Kronos was king of the Titans, who were the original gods. He married his sister, then devoured his own children when it was foretold that one of them would overthrow him. But one son, Zeus, escaped and eventually returned to defeat him. Zeus later became chief of all the gods.

● The *Kronosaurus* remains found on the Harvard expedition in 1931–32 were blasted out of the rock by the expedition leader's assistant – a man known as 'the maniac' for his enthusiastic use of dynamite.

2 Another possibility is that the *Kronosaurus* gave birth to live young in the water. Fossils have been found of other marine reptiles, called icthyosaurs, giving birth like this.

OURANOSAURUS

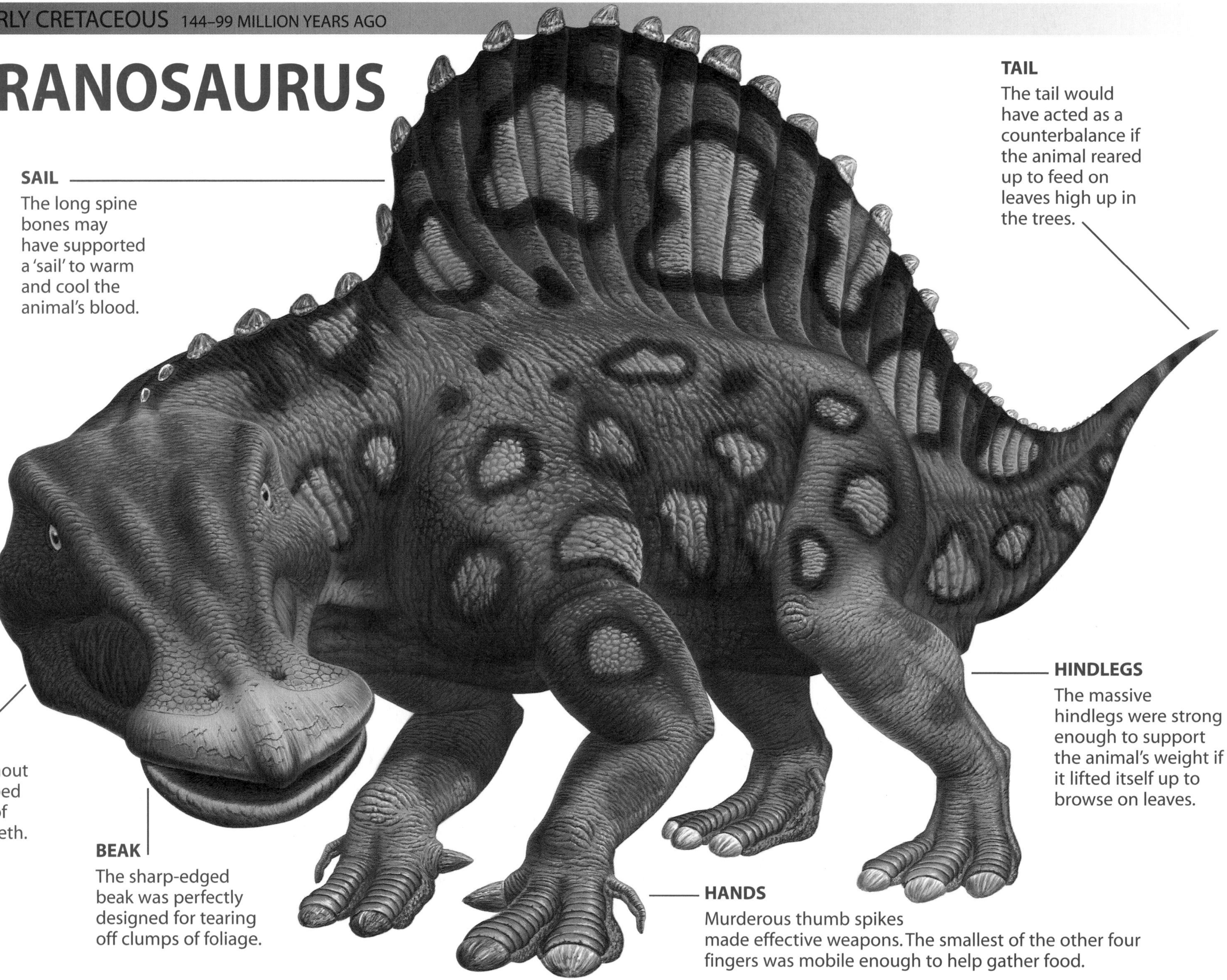

SAIL

The long spine bones may have supported a 'sail' to warm and cool the animal's blood.

TAIL

The tail would have acted as a counterbalance if the animal reared up to feed on leaves high up in the trees.

JAWS

The long snout was equipped with rows of grinding teeth.

BEAK

The sharp-edged beak was perfectly designed for tearing off clumps of foliage.

HINDLEGS

The massive hindlegs were strong enough to support the animal's weight if it lifted itself up to browse on leaves.

HANDS

Murderous thumb spikes made effective weapons. The smallest of the other four fingers was mobile enough to help gather food.

This big, heavy, plant-eating dinosaur had powerful jaws perfect for tearing off and grinding up leaves. Fossil remains show that *Ouranosaurus* had extra-long spinal bones on its back. Some experts think that the bones supported a tall sail that the reptile used to maintain a comfortable temperature. In the early morning, the animal could warm up by standing with its sail facing the sun. The sail may also have been brightly patterned and used as a displays to attract potential mates.

Ouranosaurus was armed with a pair of deadly hand spikes to defend itself from meat-eating predators.

HOW BIG WAS IT?

DINO FACTS

LENGTH	Up to 7m	
WEIGHT	Up to 2 tonnes	
DIET	Mainly leaves and shoots	
DEFENCES	Strong spikes on front feet	The remains of *Ouranosaurus* have been found in the sands of the Sahara Desert, in Africa. At the time when *Ouranosaurus* lived, 100 million years ago, this region was almost as hot as it is now.
MEANING OF NAME	'Valiant lizard'	

1 A brightly coloured sail could be very useful for a dinosaur. Like a chameleon, *Ouranosaurus* might have altered the pattern on its sail, to deter rivals or impress a mate. By changing the sail's colour, it might also have controlled its temperature.

Did You Know?

● *Ouranosaurus* comes from an Arab word, *ourane*. This is what the nomadic tribespeople of the Sahara Desert call the local sand monitor lizards.

● The skull of *Ouranosaurus* has a pair of bumps on the nose that have no obvious function. It is possible that they are sexual features found only on males, and that a female skull has not so far been found.

● *Ouranosaurus* lived before modern flowering plants appeared, so it probably fed on the foliage of plants such as horsetails, gingkoes, cycads, ferns and young conifers.

2 Some researchers think the spinal bones supported a great hump. The hump might have been a fat store, to help the reptile survive food shortages.

PSITTACOSAURUS

COLOUR
Some experts believe that *Psittacosaurus* relied on cunning camouflage to hide from hungry killer dinosaurs.

TAIL
The beast may have used this as a balancing rod when rearing on its hindlegs.

ARMS
These were long enough to use to pass food to its mouth.

BILL
This was formed from horn covering bone. At its tip was a rostral bone, a feature unique to horned dinosaurs.

This scary-looking but harmless animal once lived in great numbers all over eastern Asia. It had a sharp, parrot-like bill to strip off leaves, and long arms to pull down branches. It must have spent most of its waking hours munching on plants, as it would have needed to swallow large amounts to get enough energy.

Experts believe that it may have gathered in huge herds to dissuade attackers.

HOW BIG WAS IT?

DINO FACTS

SIZE	Length about 2m; shoulder height 1m; weight 50kg
DIET	Tough, low-growing plants
DEFENCES	Sharp, powerful beak, and possibly skills herding
MEANING OF NAME	'Parrot lizard'

Psittacosaurus was an incredibly successful dinosaur, making up 90 per cent of the fossil record in some parts of Mongolia. Its fossil remains have also been found at various sites in China, as well as in Thailand and Russia.

Three adults are feasting in the warm Mongolian sun. One of the dinosaurs rears on its hindlegs, pulls down a low branch with its arms, and wolfs down mouthful after mouthful of thick leaves. Another of the beasts picks up some fallen pine cones, cracking them apart to eat the tasty insides.

1

Having finished its banquet, the third of the *Psittacosaurus* reaches down to swallow some pebbles. These *gastroliths* will help grind up the tough food in the animal's stomach.

2

Did You Know?

● The first *Psittacosaurus* fossil was found in 1922, on the American Museum of Natural History's third expedition to Mongolia, and named the next year by US expert Henry Fairfield Osborn.

● It was discovered alongside the remains of another dinosaur, which Osborn initially thought was quite different. This second set of remains was eventually reclassified as being another *Psittacosaurus*.

● Some *Psittacosaurus* fossils contain smoothly polished pebbles, proving that the dinosaurs deliberately swallowed stones to aid its digestion. In the same way, birds such as pigeons and budgies today swallow grit to grind up food.

PTERODAUSTRO

WINGS
The wings were made of skin strengthened with tough fibres.

EYES
Pterodaustro, like all pterosaurs, had well-developed eyesight but a poor sense of smell. Good vision was more useful for detecting plankton swarms in the waters far below.

FEET
Four of the five toes were long and tipped with claws. They probably helped the animal to grip clifftop roost sites.

JAWS
These were lined with hundreds of narrow teeth. These were used to filter tiny plants and animals from the water.

FINGERS
The long fourth finger supported the leathery wing. The other three fingers were short and clawed.

One of the oddest of all flying reptiles, this beast's long, upturned jaws were lined with up to 500 thin, bendy teeth ideal for filtering food from the water.

Pterodaustro once patrolled the skies of South America while huge dinosaurs roamed the land beneath. Its wings were made of tough, leathery skin supported by the long fourth fingers.

Its amazing bill allowed it to scoop up vast quantities of plankton, the tiny plants and animals that would have filled the seas and the lakes of the time.

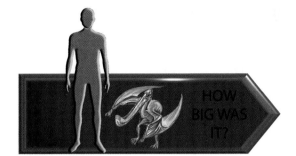

HOW BIG WAS IT?

DINO FACTS

WINGSPAN	Up to 1.5m	*Pterodaustro* was the first prehistoric flying reptile to be discovered in South America. Fossil expert José Bonaparte found a few of the pterosaur's bones in rocks in Argentina in 1970, then a complete but crushed skeleton. Similar remains have been discovered in Chile, and footprints like those of *Pterodaustro* were found in France, so the reptile may have been more widespread.
SKULL LENGTH	About 25cm	
DIET	Mainly plant and animal plankton	
MEANING OF NAME	'Wing of the south'	

FEEDING TIME

A group of *Pterodaustro* is feeding in the shallow waters of a lake. Clouds of mud swirl around the reptiles' feet as they stamp up and down to disturb the little creatures hidden in the lake bed. They lower their jaws into the water and scoop up the soupy mixture.

Did You Know?

● *Pterodaustro*'s wings may have been infested with parasites, which would have sucked blood from the many fine blood vessels inside the wing membrane. *Pterodaustro* would have had to groom itself for hours to remove these parasites and keep its wings in tiptop flight condition.

● *Pterodaustro*'s discoverer José Bonaparte has been called 'master of the Mesozoic' because of the large number of fossil discoveries relating to that geological era that he made in South America.

● When Italian zoologist Cosimo Collini saw the first pterosaur fossils discovered in the late 18th century he thought they probably belonged to a sea creature; however, later experts believed they belonged to an early kind of bat or gliding lizard.

SPINOSAURUS

SAIL

Experts think it unlikely that sail-backed *Spinosaurus* males fought each other often. Such duels would have risked damaging their spines.

SPINE

Blade-like spines extended from the dinosaur's strong backbone.

COLOUR

No one knows for sure, but *Spinosaurus* might have had brightly coloured stripes for camouflage.

TAIL

The long tail helped balance the weight of the dinosaur's heavy upper body.

SKULL

No complete fossils of the skull of *Spinosaurus* exist. Most experts think the dinosaur had jaws like a crocodile.

HINDLEGS

Powerful hindlegs would have propelled *Spinosaurus* along at great speed.

TEETH

The long teeth of *Spinosaurus* were as sharp as a butcher's knives.

ARMS

The arms of *Spinosaurus* were slightly longer than those of most other carnivorous dinosaurs. The creature may sometimes have walked on all fours.

O ne of the biggest of all carnivorous dinosaurs, the *Spinosaurus* was a powerful meat-eater. It tore at its victims with massive, crocodile-like jaws and rows of needle-sharp teeth. It may have found food by attacking plant-eating dinosaurs, scavenging dead carcasses or even cannibalizing its own kind.

On its back, tall spines were probably covered with skin, giving this dinosaur a bizarre sail. The sail may have been rich in blood vessels that could help *Spinosaurus* warm itself into activity.

HOW BIG WAS IT?

DINO FACTS

LENGTH	Up to 15m
WEIGHT	Up to 4 tonnes
SPINES	Up to 1.8m long
WEAPONS	Long, sharp teeth and probably sharp claws
DIET	Other dinosaurs, dead or alive, and probably dinosaur eggs as well
MEANING OF NAME	'Thorn lizard'

Remains of *Spinosaurus* have been discovered throughout northern Africa, in the areas now known as Egypt, Morocco, Tunisia and Niger. In the middle of the Cretaceous, when *Spinosaurus* lived, these areas were flood plains covered with lush forests.

If *Spinosaurus* chanced upon a dead dinosaur it would have wasted no time. Its long jaws were perfect for delving into a decomposing body.

2

1

Plant-eating *Ouranosaurus* was no match for *Spinosaurus*. The peaceful plant-eater would been almost defenceless against the powerful jaws and sharp teeth of the hungry hunter.

Did You Know?

● Fossils of another dinosaur closely related to *Spinosaurus* were found in the Sahara Desert in 1998. Named *Suchomimus*, this creature had long, narrow jaws but, unlike *Spinosaurus*, had a row of small spikes on its back instead of a tall sail.

● Some dinosaur experts think that the spines of *Spinosaurus* supported a hump of fat, similar to that of camels today, rather than a sail. The hump may have helped protect the dinosaur from the heat of its northern African homeland and could also have acted as a vital energy reserve in times when food was scarce.

3 Hungry *Spinosaurus* would have felt no guilt about stealing from a nest full of *Spinosaurus* eggs. In several swift lunges, the beast could have snapped up as many defenceless baby dinosaurs and unhatched eggs as it could fit in its stomach.

SUCHOMIMUS

BODY
Suchomimus probably hunted like a crocodile, but its body plan was closer to that of a land hunter such as *T. rex*.

NOSTRILS
These sat on top of the snout, like a crocodile's, enabling the killer to lie hidden in water.

TAIL
The long, strong tail was powerful enough to propel the predator through the water in pursuit of prey.

FORELIMBS
The front limbs were short but horribly well armed. Each thumb was capped with a huge, curved claw.

TEETH
The teeth of *Suchomimus* were perfect for catching fish. They locked tightly together, creating a narrow mesh from which even the slipperiest fish could not escape.

Around 100 million years ago a killer dinosaur, armed with hook-like teeth and terrifying claws, terrorized the waters of Africa, ambushing other dinosaurs and huge fish.

Suchomimus probably waded into the water on its two legs and impaled giant fish on the massive claws on its thumbs. It may also have hidden in the rushes, waiting for a dinosaur to bend down to drink. In a single lunge, its powerful jaws could have crunched right through its victim's flesh and bones.

The only known specimen found was not fully grown. Had it lived, it might have been one of the biggest killer dinosaurs of all time.

Did You Know?

● *Suchomimus* was a member of the spinosaurid family. This was one of the most successful of all groups of land predators, found throughout Africa, Europe and North America.

● The dinosaur experts who found *Suchomimus* spent over two months searching for fossils in the baking desert heat. But it was well worth it. As well as *Suchomimus*, they found the remains of 15m-long crocodiles, giant fish and huge flying reptiles.

● *Suchomimus* had spines along its back that some experts think were fleshed out with a 'sail'. This sail may have been brightly coloured for use in mating displays, or it may have absorbed the sun's early morning rays so that the 'cold-blooded' beast would have warmed up quickly to prey on still-sluggish plant-eaters.

HOW BIG WAS IT?

Wading through water, a large *Suchomimus* spots a shoal of plump, juicy fish. With a quick swipe of his vicious thumb-claw, he spears a fish and tears it in half.

1

A young male appears, eager to join the feast. Furious, the larger reptile lashes out at his rival's throat. The youngster runs off, bleeding from his wound.

2

DINO FACTS

SIZE	11m long; 4m high at the hip	Scientists found the only known *Suchomimus* skeleton in the southern Sahara Desert, in Niger, Central Africa. The killer probably spent most of its time swimming or wading in the rivers and swamps that crisscrossed this area over 90 million years ago. But *Suchomimus* may have been widespread over most of Africa.
DIET	Probably large fish and dinosaurs, dead or alive	
MEANING OF NAME	'Crocodile mimic'	

UTAHRAPTOR

HINDLIMBS
The legs provided the speed and power needed to lash out with the long killing claws.

EYES
Large eyes helped *Utahraptor* to stalk its quarry.

SICKLE CLAW
The trademark of the raptor is the killing sickle claw on the second of the four toes of either foot. Usually swivelled upwards out of the way, the claw swings into place for the kill.

HAND CLAWS
The three long claws on the end of each forelimb were broad, flattened and sharp, and could have inflicted slashing wounds as well as securing a hold.

HEAD
Utahraptor's big head housed the largest brain, relative to body size, of any known dinosaur. This was a highly intelligent hunter.

TEETH
The rows of saw-edged teeth were designed to cut through tough flesh. New teeth grew to replace any that broke off during the attack.

One of the fiercest of all flesh-eating dinosaurs, this big, long-clawed beast was fast enough to capture and devour big and small prey. *Utahraptor* ran like a sprinter on its large, strong back legs, before pouncing on its victim. It would lash out with its long, hinged hind claws. Powerful jaws lined with serrated teeth allowed it to rip chunks of flesh from its victims. Experts believe that *Utahraptors* may have hunted in packs, using their superior speed and cunning to trap a terrified animal.

HOW BIG WAS IT?

A pack of *Utahraptors* follows a herd of grazing *Iguanodons* for days, looking for one that is weakened by age or sickness. When they decide on their target, the killers secretly surround the victim. Suddenly they spring at the poor beast from all sides.

1

2 The animal's end is swift but savage. Lashing out with their huge toe claws, the predators open up the hapless animal's belly. They then gather around the kill to feast on fresh, bloody flesh.

DINO FACTS

LENGTH	5–7m	Scientists found all known *Utahraptor* fossils in and around Arches National Park, in eastern Utah, USA. Now a rock and desert wilderness, the area would have been fertile savannah 125 million years ago, when *Utahraptor* dwelt there. The beast probably hunted a region now covered by the states of Arizona and Colorado, as well as Utah.
WEIGHT	500–1000kg	
PREY	Plant-eating dinosaurs	
WEAPONS	25–35cm slashing claws	
MEANING OF NAME	'Robber from Utah'	

Did You Know?

● The first *Utahraptor* fossil was unearthed in 1991. Amazed scientists found massive bones and claws in a quarry near Moab, eastern Utah.

● *Utahraptor* rivals the size of the giant *Velociraptors* shown in the film *Jurassic Park*. At the time of the movie's release, just a year before *Utahraptor*'s discovery, scientists had scoffed at the huge dinosaur being depicted on screen, saying it was twice the size of any known member of the Dromaeosauridae.

● In 1995, scientists in Madagascar discovered the fossil of a primitive bird with a retractable sickle claw on the second toe of each foot, just like *Utahraptor*. This find reinforces the theory held by some scientists that birds are descended from dinosaurs.

The Late Cretaceous Period

The second half of the Cretaceous period lasted until around 65 million years ago and was the last great age of the dinosaurs. At the end of this period, a great extinction killed off the dinosaurs forever.

Before the Cretaceous period, the Earth looked quite different from the way it looks today. But this soon started to change. In the late Cretaceous period the climate began to cool, and many of the world's huge mountain ranges formed. Many types of insects we would recognize today began to appear, such as ants, butterflies and bees.

We would also recognize some of the big reptiles of the time. Huge *Deinosuchus* was clearly a crocodile, even though it was over twice as large as any crocodiles alive today. Other reptiles lost some of their dinosaur looks. Mosasaurs, for instance, had big dinosaur heads and fish-like bodies. Not all the big reptiles changed so much. After all, this was the age of dinosaurs such as *Tyrannosaurus rex*, the fearsome killer with sharp, dagger-like teeth.

Dinosaurs dominated the late Cretaceous world, but their age was almost at an end. Around 65 million years ago, there was a mass extinction and millions of creatures died. Among them were the dinosaurs. They had been around for 165 million years, but now their time was over.

CARNOTAURUS

HORNS

These were made of thick layers of horn and solid bone. Only the bone fossilized.

SKIN

The creature's tough skin was covered with rows of studs and scales, probably to protect it from rivals.

TAIL

The strong tail would have balanced the heavy front of the dinosaur's body as it ran.

EYES

The dinosaur's eyes faced forwards to give the creature 'binocular vision', which helps when judging distances: a useful skill for an active hunter.

BACK LEGS

The powerful back legs would have carried the killer at speed.

JAWS

Carnotaurus' jaws were lined with slender, curving 4cm-long teeth. To fossil experts, the lower jaw seems too narrow and weak for a killer dinosaur.

Carnotaurus was a horned killer that once prowled the plains of South America. With its sharp eyes and vicious teeth and claws, it was well equipped to hunt down its victims. Tough scales and pebbly studs covered the animal's thick hide and may have helped to protect it from rivals.

Carnotaurus' most striking features were its solid-looking head and cow-like horns. The horns may have been used by males in head-butting contests.

No one knows how this dinosaur bred. Perhaps it let its young hatch on their own. Or maybe it reared them carefully.

HOW BIG WAS IT?

DINO FACTS

LENGTH	Up to 7.5m	
WEIGHT	About 1 tonne	
DIET	Smaller dinos, dead or alive	
WEAPONS	Sharp teeth and claws	
MEANING OF NAME	'Meat-eating bull'	

An almost complete skeleton of Carnotaurus was discovered in 1985 in Patagonia, Argentina, in South America, by a team led by the famed Argentinian dinosaur expert José Bonaparte. Carnotaurus' remains were so well preserved that there were skin impressions from parts of the body. Fossil hunters have since found a second well-preserved Carnotaurus in the same region.

1 A male Carnotaurus scoops earth out of the ground to form a hollow mound. Soon a female he mated earlier lays eggs in his nest. Other mates then add eggs to the pile, and the male covers each batch with ferns to keep them warm.

2 The male keeps watch over his precious clutch, adding more ferns at nightfall when the air temperature starts to drop, removing them again in the morning. Once his brood has hatched, he continues to guard them. At first the young killer dinosaurs stay behind while their father goes hunting. The big male drags his prey back to the nest for the hungry pack to feast on.

3 When the squealing youngsters have eaten their fill they follow their father as he leads them to water to drink. Once his babies have grown larger they will go with him on his hunting trips, to watch him chase and kill, so they can learn how to catch food for themselves.

Did You Know?

● Carnotaurus is thought to belong to the Abelisauridae dinosaur family. These big flesh-eaters all moved on their hindlegs and had big, powerful heads. Several had horns. All the abelisaurs discovered so far lived in South America, Africa and India. When the dinosaurs were alive, India was located south of the equator.

● In addition to the other strange features that have so baffled the experts, some of Carnotaurus' spinal bones had odd wing-like projections never seen in other dinosaurs. Fossil experts have no idea what their function might have been.

● Carnotaurus features in the film The Lost World: Jurassic Park II (1997). In this epic fantasy, the dinosaur is capable of quite amazing changes of colour, rather like a chameleon.

DEINOCHEIRUS

FOREARMS

Long and powerful forearms may have allowed *Deinocheirus* to pull off tree branches and feast on the leaves.

CLAWS

Deinocheirus' huge claws could have had various functions, as tools or weapons. Some experts believe *Deinocheirus* ripped open termite mounds to get at the insects inside, the way an anteater still does today.

TAIL

The long, heavy tail would have been held out straight to counterbalance the head, neck and forelimbs, as the beast sped over the ground.

TALONS

Deinocheirus could have slashed at its prey, inflicting lethal damage with a single stroke of its claws. The terrifying talons, swinging through the air like scythes, would have made formidable weapons.

BEAK

It would have had a strong, sharp beak, ideal for stripping tree branches – or ripping flesh.

FEET

The huge feet probably had three splayed toes. Sharp toe claws could have provided additional slashing weapons.

LEGS

Deinocheirus would have walked upright so, to bear its heavy frame, the legs needed to be huge, with mighty muscles and pillar-like bones.

All that has been found of this immense dinosaur are two vast clawed arms, so scientists can only speculate as to what the rest of its body would have looked like.

Some experts think *Deinocheirus* fed on tree leaves, using its powerful forelimbs to rip off the branches. Others believe it feasted on meat, living or dead, using its dagger-like claws to slice off great chunks of flesh.

HOW BIG WAS IT?

DINO FACTS

HEIGHT	Possibly 6–10m
WEIGHT	Possibly 7–10 tonnes
DIET	Possibly vegetation such as leaves; may have dined on animals, dead or alive
MEANING OF NAME	'Terrible hand'

The arms of *Deinocheirus mirificus* were found in Ömnögovî, in southern Mongolia. This region is a treasure trove of fossils such as *Gallimimus*, an ostrich-like dinosaur thought to be a relative of *Deinocheirus*. Fossil hunters also unearthed here the huge clawed arms of a dinosaur called *Therizinosaurus*, but, again, its body was absent.

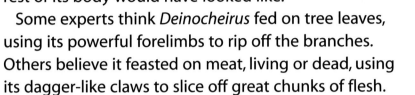

1   Gripping a thick tree limb with its big fingers, *Deinocheirus* pulls the branch downwards and begins to feast on the succulent young leaves.

2   A killer *Segnosaurus* leaps from cover and startles the feeding *Deinocheirus*. The leaf-eater stands firm, and with one blow it sends the attacker reeling, with blood spurting from a fatal head wound.

Did You Know?

● The skin of *Deinocheirus* could have been covered in scales, like that of a lizard. The dinosaur might have been camouflaged for hiding from enemies, or brightly coloured to attract a mate and deter rivals.

● The main threat to *Deinocheirus* would have come from the meat-eating dinosaur *Tarbosaurus*, an Asian relative of *Tyrannosaurus rex*.

● Some experts think *Deinocheirus* actually lived in trees, like the South American sloth. Researchers have even reconstructed the dinosaur as a giant tree-climber clinging by its hefty arms. However, *Deinocheirus* would have needed a gigantic tree to support its weight. A more likely comparison may be the giant ground sloth, a non-climbing leaf-eater that lived about one million years ago.

DEINOSUCHUS

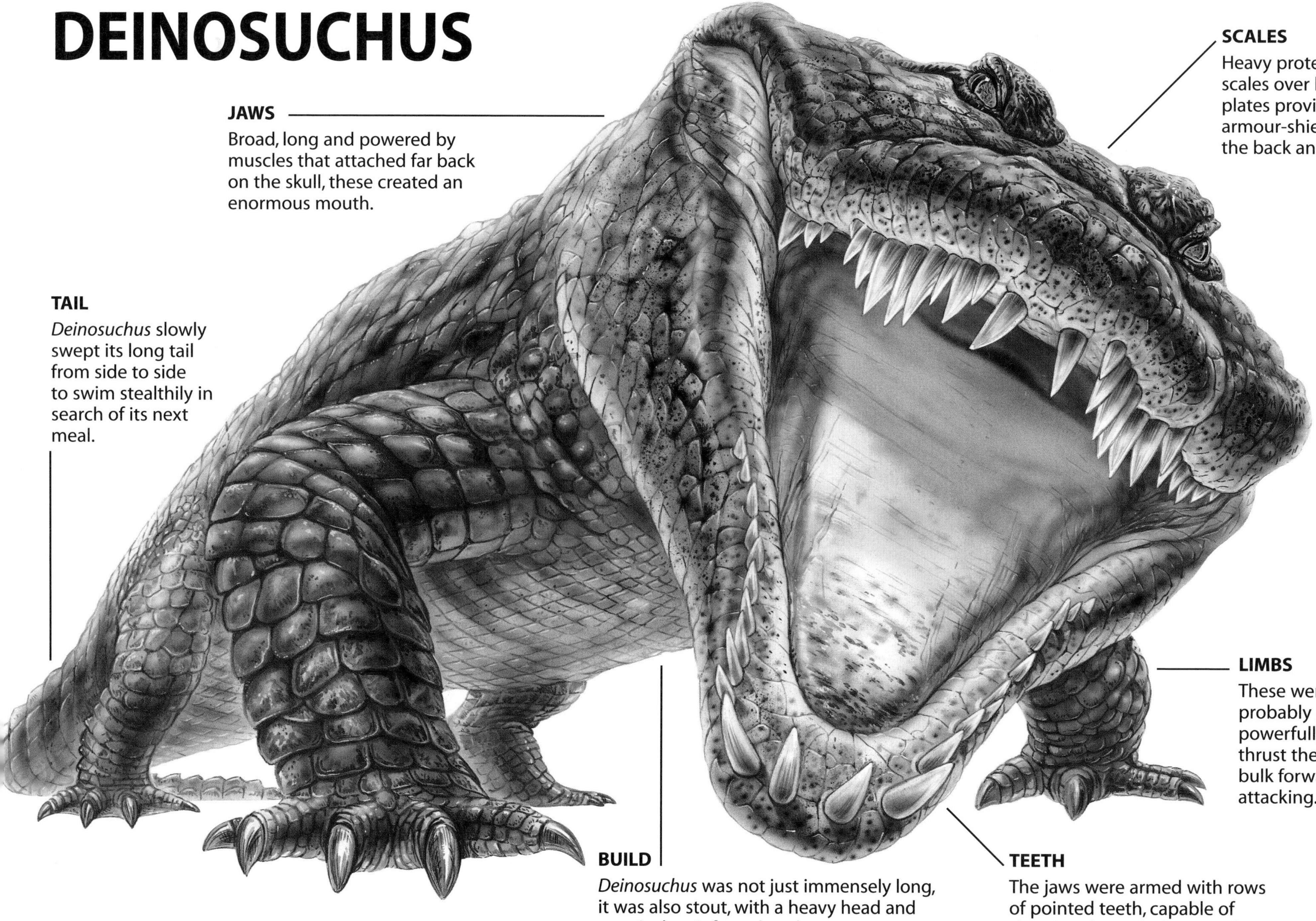

JAWS

Broad, long and powered by muscles that attached far back on the skull, these created an enormous mouth.

SCALES

Heavy protective scales over bony plates provided armour-shielding for the back and tail.

TAIL

Deinosuchus slowly swept its long tail from side to side to swim stealthily in search of its next meal.

LIMBS

These were probably short and powerfully built, to thrust the animal's bulk forward when attacking.

BUILD

Deinosuchus was not just immensely long, it was also stout, with a heavy head and massively reinforced neck.

TEETH

The jaws were armed with rows of pointed teeth, capable of shearing through dinosaur flesh.

Deinosuchus was a massive-jawed crocodile that was the largest ever known to stalk the wetlands of the world. This gigantic prehistoric killing machine lurked in lush swamps and marshes in North America more than 65 million years ago. With jaws that were as long as a man's body, it could easily have tackled dinosaurs weighing several tonnes. It is easy to imagine this terrifying beast dragging a large dinosaur into the water to drown it, then wrenching off huge chunks of flesh and bone.

So far, only parts of this beast have been discovered. Scientists calculated its size from a complete skull found in Texas.

HOW BIG WAS IT?

DINO FACTS

LENGTH	12–15m, including 1.8m jaws
WEIGHT	5 tonnes
PREY	Large animals, including dinosaurs
MEANING OF NAME	'Terrible crocodile'

Deinosuchus lived in the late Cretaceous period, in swamps and marshes covering much of what is now North America. Fossil hunters have unearthed partial remains of the mighty prehistoric crocodile in Montana and Texas.

1 Hidden beneath the surface, *Deinosuchus* drifts towards a big duck-billed dinosaur grazing at the water's edge. Just as the duck-bill senses danger, the giant crocodile explodes from the water, clamps its terrible jaws around the dinosaur's throat and drags its victim into the water. After an underwater struggle, the duck-bill drowns. and the crocodile can begin its bloody feast.

Did You Know?

● *Deinosuchus* was one of an ancient line of crocodilian reptiles that have shared the same basic body plan from late Jurassic times (some 150 million years ago) right through to the present day.

● Like many modern-day crocodiles, *Deinosuchus* probably swallowed stones as ballast to counteract its body's buoyancy and help it remain submerged when sneaking up on prey.

● *Deinosuchus* is sometimes known by the alternative name *Phobosuchus*, or 'fearsome croc'.

● Based on careful studies of its scales – counting their growth rings like the rings of a tree – experts estimate that *Deinosuchus* took 35 years to reach adult size.

EDMONTONIA

ARMOUR
The skin on the head, neck, back, legs and tail was thick and leathery. It was encased in bony plates, studs and spikes. These offered protection against enemies, but also allowed the skin to bend as *Edmontonia* moved about. Only the underside lacked the bony armour.

TAIL
Like the body, the tail is studded for protection.

HEAD
Massive slabs of bone covered the skull for extra protection, forming a natural 'crash helmet'. The small eyes were protected by bony ridges above them.

SPIKES
Wicked, sharp-tipped spikes protected *Edmontonia*'s neck and flanks from the side attacks of predators.

LIMBS
The limbs were stout and pillar-like, to support the great weight of the body. The forelimbs were shorter than the hindlimbs, so that *Edmontonia* walked with its hips higher than its shoulders, and its head near the ground. This helped it feed easily on low-growing vegetation.

JAWS
The dinosaur had a few, simple, leaf-shaped teeth for biting off soft plants towards the rear of the jaws. The front of both upper and lower jaws formed a toothless, horn-covered beak.

Just as the age of the dinosaurs was drawing to a close, North America became the arena for some plant-eating dinsoaurs in very heavy armour. Among them was *Edmontonia*. Built like a tank, with a vast gut for processing huge amounts of foliage, *Edmontonia* must have moved very slowly. But it had little to fear from predators – its colossal size and impressive body armour were enough to put off most attackers. A studded upper hide turned this dinosaur into an impregnable fortress. Any predator foolish enough to try tearing a chunk out of *Edmontonia* risked snapping a tooth off or goring itself on a spike.

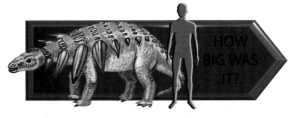

HOW BIG WAS IT?

1 *Albertosaurus* is like a smaller but equally vicious version of *Tyrannosaurus rex*. As it races up to *Edmontonia* with jaws open, the bulky plant-eater looks relaxed. It is too slow to flee, so it will somehow have to sit out the attack.

DINO FACTS

LENGTH	About 7m
HEIGHT	About 1.5m
WEIGHT	Almost 3 tonnes
DIET	Ferns and other soft plants
MEANING OF NAME	'Of Edmonton', after the rock formation in Canada.

Edmontonia fossils have been found at sites in the Red Deer River region of Alberta, Canada. Other fossils found in Montana, South Dakota and Texas in the USA may be those of *Edmontonia*, but scientists can not yet say for sure.

Albertosaurus closes in for the kill, and *Edmontonia* hunkers down to guard its soft belly. But at the last moment, with death just moments away, it lurches up to impale its enemy on a long flank spike.

2

Did You Know?

● The remains of *Edmontonia* were found by George Paterson, a driver with the 1924 Geological Survey of Canada expedition to Alberta.

● *Edmontonia* was one of the last dinosaurs to live on Earth. It survived until about 65 million years ago, the date which marked the end of the age of dinosaurs.

● *Edmontonia* may have had large cheek pouches in which it could store a mass of pulpy food, to be digested later.

● In 1977, scientists found their first Australian dinosaur fossil. *Minmi* was an ankylosaur (armoured dinosaur), and therefore a cousin of *Edmontonia*. Just as exciting was the first dinosaur find in Antarctica in 1988: again, it was an ankylosaur.

EUOPLOCEPHALUS

HORNS
Short horns on the back of the head and along the back deflected predators' teeth and claws.

TAIL
Bony tendons strengthened the end of the tail, absorbing blows dealt by the hefty club at the tip.

SKIN
Thick plates of bone set in leathery skin covered all of the dinosaur's body except for its belly. In between were smaller bony nodules that continued along the legs and tail.

LEGS
These were sturdy, short and slightly longer at the back, tilting the dinosaur's nose to the ground, towards the low-growing plants it ate.

HEAD
Heavy slabs of fused bone formed a hard casing around the dinosaur's head – even its eyes had bony shutters.

JAWS
Euoplocephalus bit off leaves and lichen with its toothless beak and chomped them up with small, ridged teeth at the back of its jaws.

FEET
Broad and flat, with horny toenails, these supported the weighty, armoured body as the dinosaur stomped along.

This armour-plated, plant-eating dinosaur had a fearsome weapon, a huge ball of bone on its tail, which could shatter bones with one mighty, well-aimed blow, crippling an attacker for life.

Thick slabs of bone covered *Euoplocephalus*' head, while bands of bony nodules and spikes protected the rest of its vast, tank-like body. Even its eyelids were bony, dropping down to protected its vulnerable eyes in times of danger.

Despite its bulk and heavy coat, *Euoplocephalus* was fairly nimble and would have been able to lumber off at a jog or twist, and turn to avoid predators such as *Tyrannosaurus rex*.

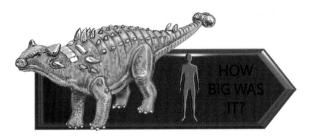

HOW BIG WAS IT?

As a *Euoplocephalus* strips the leaves from a forest fern, her sensitive nose scents danger. She turns to see her greatest enemy, *T. rex*, sidling up through the trees.

1

DINO FACTS

LENGTH	6m	In the late Cretaceous, *Euoplocephalus* was one of the most abundant armoured dinosaur in western North America. Lawrence Lambe discovered the first fossil in 1902, in Alberta, Canada. Since then, more than 40 other specimens have been found.
WEIGHT	About 2 tonnes	
DIET	Low-growing plants	
DEFENCES	Tail club and armour plating	
MEANING OF NAME	'Well-armoured head'	

Did You Know?

● Initially, Lawrence Lambe called his dinosaur *Stereocephalus*, or 'twin head'. But when he found this name had already been given to an insect, he renamed his find *Euoplocephalus*.

● *Euoplocephalus*' hefty, club-like tail weighed as much as 30kg – about the same as 60 jars of jam.

● *Euoplocephalus* may well have had a fermentation chamber in its stomach, like that of a cow today, to help it digest all the tough plant fibre. And like a cow, it probably let off vast amounts of gas.

● *Euoplocephalus*' stocky legs were positioned well under its body, more like those of a mammal than a reptile.

2 Quickly, she turns her back on the killer and crouches low to the ground to protect her soft belly, lashing her bone-tipped tail back and forth. The predator circles its intended victim, hoping to turn the *Euoplocephalus* over, but she keeps shuffling around. Finally, it lunges forwards in frustration, and the *Euoplocephalus* lands a hefty blow to its nose. Her attacker skulks off, bleeding heavily from the snout.

GALLIMIMUS

BEAK
Flattened, toothless jaws were edged with horn, forming a sort of beak.

TAIL
As *Gallimimus* ran, it held its slender tail straight out behind, creating a counter balance for the short body.

HINDLEGS
Gallimimus walked upright on powerful hindlegs. If alarmed, the dinosaur could reach considerable speeds over short distances.

NECK
A long, flexible neck enabled *Gallimimus* to make quick, darting movements with its head, so that it could catch small, swift-moving prey.

HANDS
The hands ended in three fingers tipped with claws, but they were weak and *Gallimimus* could not grip strongly.

HINDFEET
Narrow feet with long toes were lightweight, and could be moved with ease. Only the outer two toes touched the ground when *Gallimimus* sprinted away.

Nimble and long-legged, *Gallimimus* was an Olympic sprinter of a dinosaur. Few predators could have caught the bird-like beast as it sped along. *Gallimimus* was half bird and half lizard, with a long, stiff tail, legs like an ostrich and a toothless beak. Loping along on its hind legs, it snapped up small creatures such as lizards and perhaps even the buried eggs of other dinosaurs in a ceaseless quest for food.

HOW BIG WAS IT?

DINO FACTS

LENGTH	5.6m
HEIGHT	3m at head; 2m at hip
WEIGHT	250kg
SPEED	Up to 100km/h
DIET	Plants, insects, eggs and small vertebrates such as lizards
MEANING OF NAME	'Bird mimic'

Gallimimus was discovered by a team of Russian scientists in 1972, at Bayshin Tsav in south–eastern Mongolia. Since the original find, more partial skeletons have been unearthed from other sites nearby.

1 Away from the herd, an adult *Gallimimus* discovers the nest of a *Saichania* dinosaur. The eggs are an excellent source of protein for the scavenger. Scrabbling at the soil with its forelimbs, *Gallimimus* uncovers the nest and pops an egg in its mouth.

Did You Know?

● Though it was previously little known, *Gallimimus* became famous in 1993 when a stampeding herd of the dinosaurs featured in the film *Jurassic Park*.

● *Gallimimus* was one of the largest members of a group of dinosaurs called ornithomimosaurs, meaning 'bird-mimicking lizards'. Early ornithomimosaurs had teeth, but by the late Cretaceous period only toothless forms remained.

● When *Gallimimus* was alive, the world's sea levels were much higher than today, and China, Mongolia and the eastern half of Russia formed a giant island.

2 Cracking each egg with its beak, *Gallimimus* guzzles the gooey contents. But soon it spots movement in the distance.

3 A larger predator is heading towards the plundered nest. Unwilling to risk a fight, *Gallimimus* grabs one last egg in its beak and speeds off with long strides.

HESPERORNIS

EYES

These may have been adapted for keen underwater vision, giving the bird poor surface eyesight.

FEATHERS

Who knows what colour these were? Most birds have oily, waterproof plumage. But cormorants do not, to make diving easier, so perhaps *Hesperornis* did not either.

WINGS

The bird would have used its short wings as rudders for sudden, nifty changes of direction when pursuing prey.

BILL

This was long and slim, giving *Hesperornis* extra reach to snap up fish and squid.

TONGUE

A long, narrow tongue would have helped the bird gulp down wriggling fish head-first.

TAIL

The short tail would have helped the bird twist and turn underwater with great precision.

FEET

Most experts agree that *Hesperornis* had webbed feet, like modern diving birds. The sharp claws would have provided good grip on slippery shores.

TEETH

Unlike modern birds, *Hesperornis* had teeth – lots of them. Once in their clutches, a fish would have had no chance.

Near the end of the dinosaur era, North America's shallow inland seas witnessed a new terror. This time the hunter was not a reptile, but a giant fishing bird, as much at home in the water as its prey.

Hesperornis was a flightless predator that resembled a modern-day cormorant, except that it was almost as big as a man.

It patrolled coastal waters for fish and squid, snaring them with a bill lined with wickedly sharp teeth. Its torpedo-shaped body and powerful legs made it an expert swimmer that could overtake all but the fastest prey.

HOW BIG WAS IT?

One calm day, *Hesperornis* paddles slowly along, looking for fish or squid below. The bird is momentarily distracted by *Pteranodon*, a big flying reptile that specializes in scooping fish from the surface, but it soars past.

1

Suddenly *Hesperornis* spots a plump squid deep below. The bird dives straight after the creature, propelling itself through the sea with great kicks of its feet. Opening its bill wide, the bird seizes the squid, then shoots to the surface to swallow its prize.

2

DINO FACTS

LENGTH	1.5m
PREY	Fish, squid and other marine animals
WEAPONS	Vicious long bill lined with needle-sharp teeth
MEANING OF NAME	'Regal western bird'

Fossilized *Hesperornis* bones have been found from Kansas to the Canadian Arctic, and are relatively common. This is because *Hesperornis* had quite dense bones, like other diving birds. Most birds have thin, light and partially hollow bones, so they are as light as possible for flying. Such fragile bones rarely survive as fossils.

Did You Know?

● Some modern diving birds spend up to eight minutes underwater and dive to 75m. It is likely that the much larger, more powerful *Hesperornis* easily exceeded these achievements.

● Scientists think *Hesperornis* spent most of its life at sea. On land it would have been vulnerable to predators, being a flightless waddler. It probably came ashore only to breed.

● US ornithologist (bird expert) Pierce Brodkorb believes that between 1.5 million and 2 million species of bird have existed since the first bird appeared on Earth. Today there are about 9000 species.

LAMBEOSAURUS

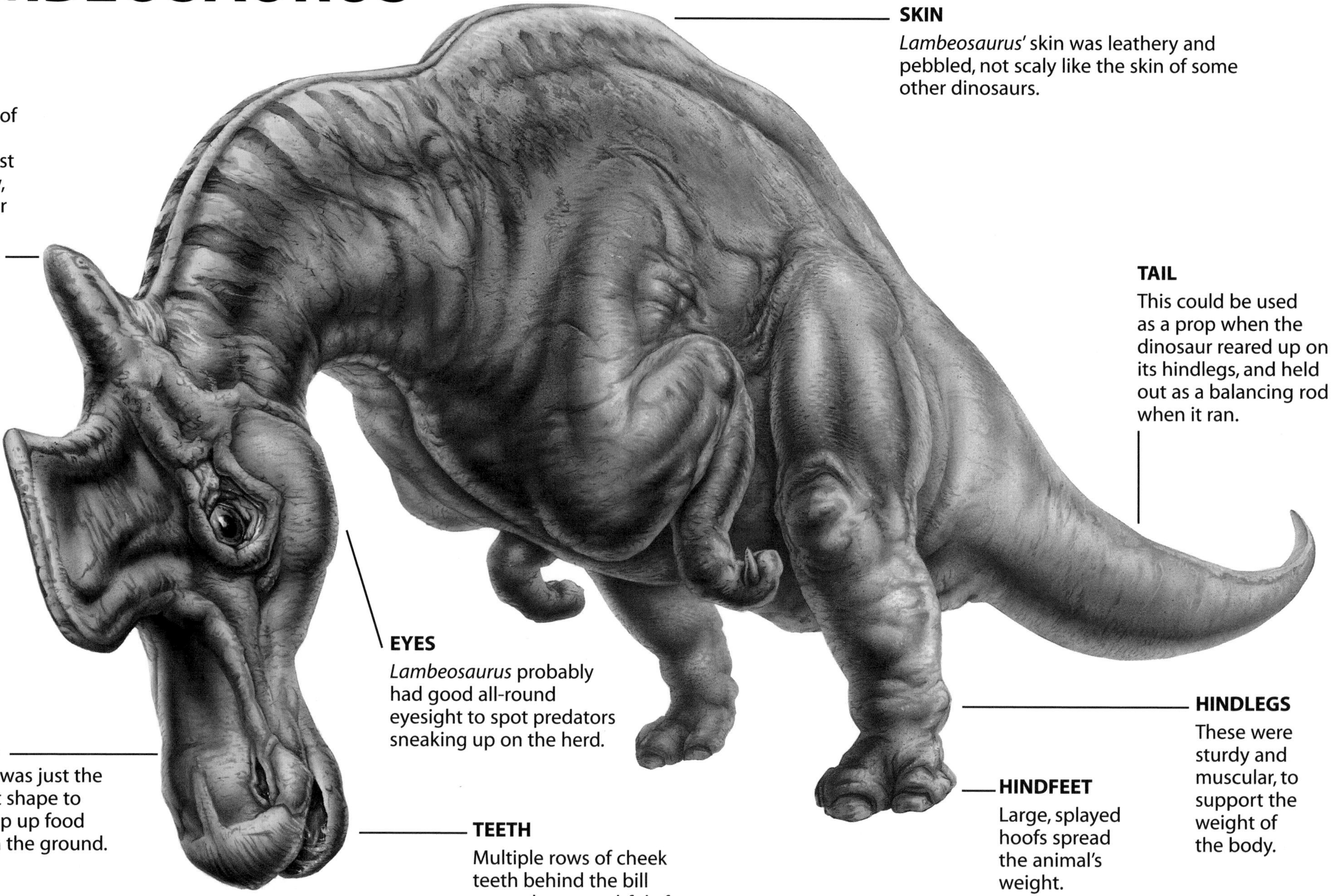

SKIN

Lambeosaurus' skin was leathery and pebbled, not scaly like the skin of some other dinosaurs.

CREST

The 'blade' of the axe-shaped crest was hollow, but the rear 'spur' was solid bone.

TAIL

This could be used as a prop when the dinosaur reared up on its hindlegs, and held out as a balancing rod when it ran.

EYES

Lambeosaurus probably had good all-round eyesight to spot predators sneaking up on the herd.

BILL

This was just the right shape to scoop up food from the ground.

TEETH

Multiple rows of cheek teeth behind the bill ground up mouthful after mouthful of coarse plants.

HINDLEGS

These were sturdy and muscular, to support the weight of the body.

HINDFEET

Large, splayed hoofs spread the animal's weight.

One of the last of all the dinosaurs, *Lambeosaurus* roamed North America in vast herds about 70 million years ago. It was a hefty, duck-billed dinosaur that usually walked on all fours, but could easily have sprinted on its hind legs to escape a rival or an enemy.

Lambeosaurus had no ordinary head – sticking out from the top of its skull were two bony structures that formed an axe-shaped head-crest. The purpose of the crest is unclear, but scientists think that it may have been used as an echo chamber to help the dinosaur to make a loud call.

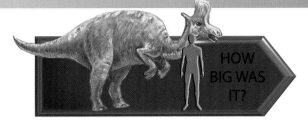

HOW BIG WAS IT?

A horde of *Lambeosaurus* try to cross a deep, fast-flowing river. Though the dinosaurs are used to wading through water, they are not so good at swimming against such a strong current – especially if the river is swollen with flood water.

1

DINO FACTS

LENGTH	9–15m, depending on species
WEIGHT	Up to 7 tonnes
DIET	Plants
MEANING OF NAME	'Lambe's lizard', after Charles Lambe, a pioneer Canadian dinosaur hunter

Fossilized remains of three species of *Lambeosaurus* – each with a different-shaped head-crest – have been found, at different sites in Alberta in Canada, Baja California in Mexico, and Montana in the USA.

Most make it across, but not all. Some of the old and the young are simply too weak, and drift downstream, drowning. Others are grabbed by lurking ancestors of crocodiles that have gathered at the spot for the feast.

2

Did You Know?

● *Lambeosaurus* lived alongside at least nine other kinds of duck-billed dinosaur of a similar size. There was plenty of food for them all, as the rise of flowering plants in the late Cretaceous vastly increased the amount of vegetation on Earth.

● Fossil remains of *Lambeosaurus* of different sizes show that the dinosaur's crest grew bigger as the animal aged.

● The tough twigs and leaves that *Lambeosaurus* ate gradually ground down its cheek-teeth. As one set of teeth wore away, another set grew below, to replace it. Elephant teeth are similar. The African elephant can replace its teeth half a dozen times. When its last set goes, it starves to death. Perhaps things were the same with duck-bills such as *Lambeosaurus*.

LIBONECTES

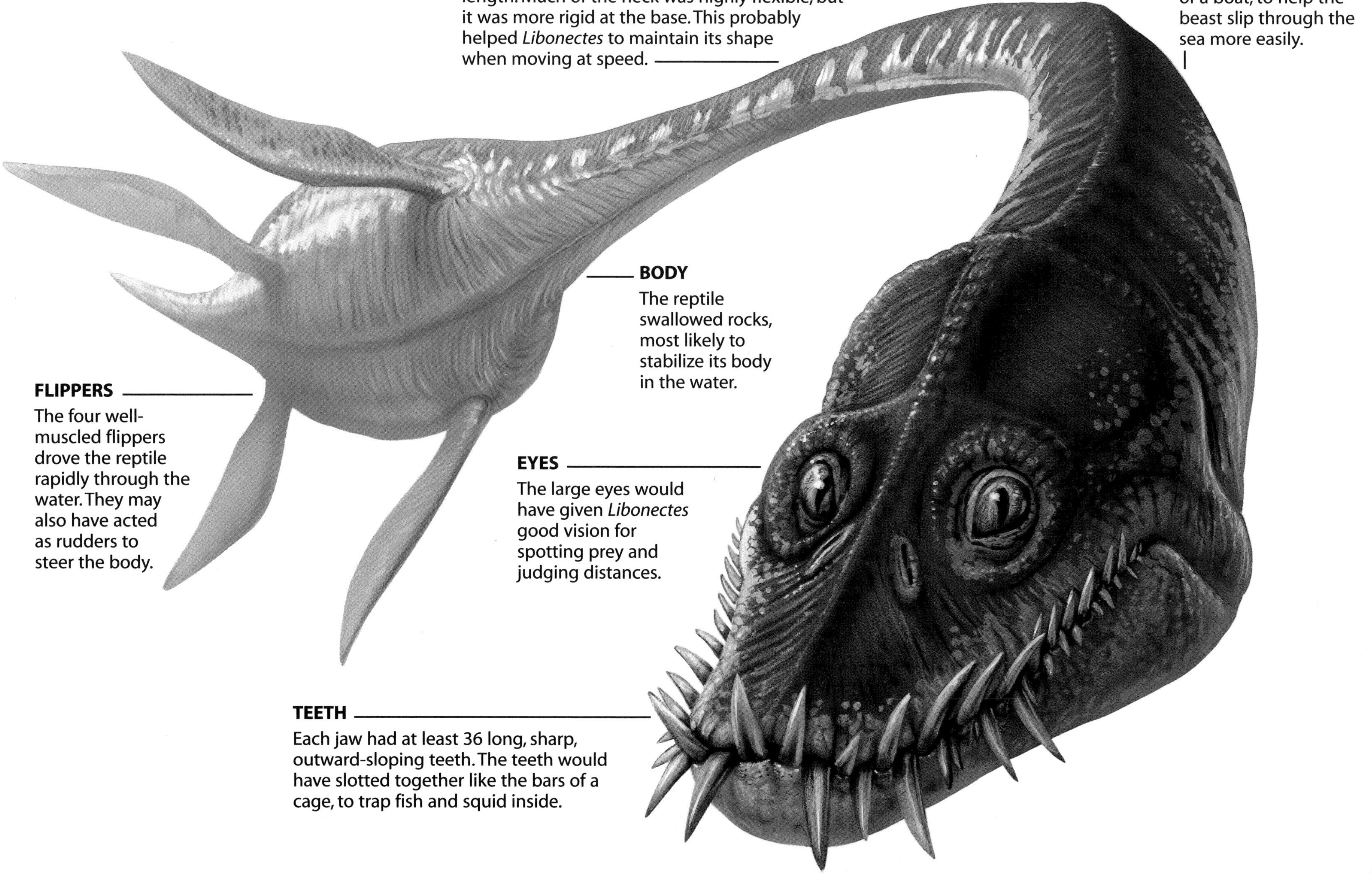

NECK

The long neck was made up of 62 bones and accounted for almost half the reptile's entire length. Much of the neck was highly flexible, but it was more rigid at the base. This probably helped *Libonectes* to maintain its shape when moving at speed.

SKIN

This would have been smooth, like the bottom of a boat, to help the beast slip through the sea more easily.

BODY

The reptile swallowed rocks, most likely to stabilize its body in the water.

FLIPPERS

The four well-muscled flippers drove the reptile rapidly through the water. They may also have acted as rudders to steer the body.

EYES

The large eyes would have given *Libonectes* good vision for spotting prey and judging distances.

TEETH

Each jaw had at least 36 long, sharp, outward-sloping teeth. The teeth would have slotted together like the bars of a cage, to trap fish and squid inside.

This amazing-looking beast with its long neck and toothy grin once prowled the ancient seas. Any prey in range of its lethal jaws had little chance of escape.

Libonectes was a member of the elasmosaur family. These marine reptiles had very long necks, powerful, paddle-like flippers, and streamlined bodies. *Libonectes* was perfectly adapted to life in the oceans and would have been capable of swimming at high speed in pursuit of the fish and squid that probably made up the bulk of its diet. Its rows of long, interconnecting teeth would have snared small sea creatures with ease.

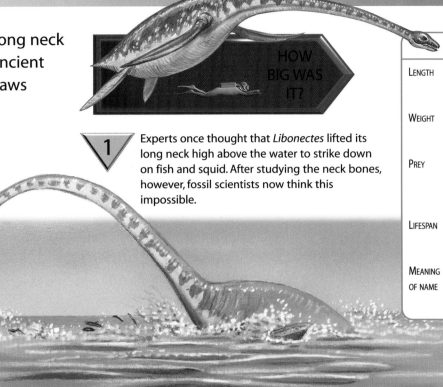

HOW BIG WAS IT?

1 Experts once thought that *Libonectes* lifted its long neck high above the water to strike down on fish and squid. After studying the neck bones, however, fossil scientists now think this impossible.

DINO FACTS

LENGTH	7–14m	
WEIGHT	5–8 tonnes	
PREY	Mainly fish and squid	
LIFESPAN	Unknown	
MEANING OF NAME	'Southwest diver'	

Fossil remains of *Libonectes* have been found in Texas and Kansas in the USA. The reptile swam in the tropical seas that existed there about 75 million years ago. The remains of other members of the elasmosaur family have been discovered at sites all over the world.

Fossil experts now think the reptile chased schools of fish and other animals through the water, whipping its head around to seize prey in its teeth-lined jaws. **2**

Did You Know?

● Elasmosaurs were once thought to lay their eggs on beaches, after pulling themselves out of the sea like turtles. New research shows the shape and weight of their body made this impossible. Perhaps they gave birth to live young, the way dolphins and many other marine mammals do today.

● *Libonectes* was very choosy about the stones that it swallowed, sometimes swimming 300km to find the kind it liked – usually an extra-hard form of igneous rock.

● We know elasmosaurs fell prey to killers such as *Mosasaurus*, for elasmosaur skulls have been found crushed and bearing the teeth marks of such big and fierce predators.

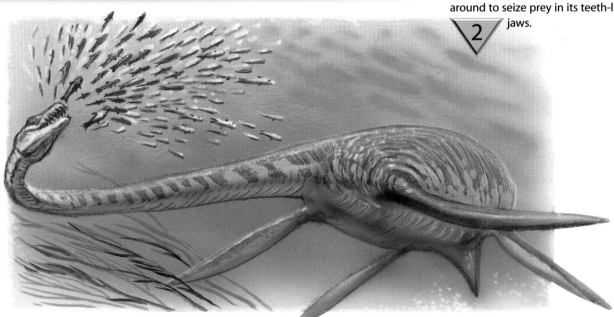

MAIASAURA

SPINE
Maiasaura's long spine was stiffened with rigid, bony tendons. This helped it hold its tail off the ground to counterbalance its weight when moving.

LEGS
The reptile could rise up on its long, pillar-like back legs to reach high foliage.

JAWS
The powerful jaws held rows of grinding teeth. As the teeth wore out, they were replaced by more teeth moving up from below.

BILL
Like other so-called duck-billed dinosaurs, *Maiasaura* had a broad, sharp-edged snout. This was ideal for cropping and collecting vast quantities of vegetation.

Eighty million years ago, immense herds of this large 'duck-billed' dinosaur roamed the plains of North America and gathered in great colonies to mate and lay eggs. Experts were forced to rethink their ideas about dinosaurs when they discovered that *Maiasaura* built nests where they fed and cared for their young, just like birds do today.

Maiasaura fossils have been found in vast numbers. In one pit alone were the remains of 10,000 of these plant-eaters that had been killed by an erupting volcano.

HOW BIG WAS IT?

DINO FACTS

SIZE	Length: up to 9m; weight: up to 3 tonnes	
DIET	Leaves and stems of plants such as ferns and cycads	
EGGS	Laid in nests in colonies	
MEANING OF NAME	'Good mother lizard'	

Maiasaura's remains were found in western Montana, near the Rocky Mountains. When *Maiasaura* was alive, 80 million years ago, this region was a fertile coastal plain on the edge of a huge ocean that once covered what are now the American prairies.

1 As it patrols the fringes of a busy *Maiasaura* nesting colony, a small *Troödon* keeps a sharp watch for nests that have been left unattended by the parents. It notices a group of adults moving off to collect food for their young.

2 Seizing its chance, the sneak-thief dashes in, grabs a baby and runs off to devour the helpless infant at leisure.

Did You Know?

● *Maiasaura* eggs were only 20cm long, but babies in the nest grew up to 1m long. The babies of migrating plant-eaters would not have stayed in the nest for more than a month or so, as local vegetation would soon be eaten by the herd. To have grown so big, so fast, they were probably 'warm-blooded' – able to generate their own heat – like mammals and birds, and not 'cold-blooded', like slow-growing modern reptiles.

● *Maiasaura*'s skull had a bony ridge that may have supported a colourful crest. If so, the male might have used the crest in courtship displays, like the 'comb' of a rooster.

● In just one mass grave, experts found 4500 fragments of *Maiasaura* bones – and had the painstaking task of fitting them all together.

MONONYKUS

FEATHERS
Mononykus was probably covered with hair-like feathers, to keep its body warm at night.

NECK
The long, flexible neck would have let *Mononykus* reach out to grab insects and lizards zigzagging across the ground or hiding in nooks and crannies.

LEGS
Long and strong, these would have helped the beast to run after prey or away from enemies.

HEAD
Mononykus probably had big eyes to spot scuttling lizards and insects, and a sharp beak to snap them up. The beak may have been lined with small, spiky teeth.

FEET
These were clawed for grip – and maybe for lashing out at attackers too.

CLAWS
Sharp and strong, these would have made short work of termite mounds, which termites build up from the ground out of damp mud, but which the sun dries as hard as concrete.

*M*ononykus was a speedy hunter that sprinted around on its long, powerful legs, feeding on lizards, insects and small mammals that it snapped up in its beak. *Mononykus* looked like a cross between a dinosaur and a bird. It had the long neck and tail of a dinosaur, but other features suggest that it evolved from an ancient flying bird. It also had two short 'arms' that puzzled scientists, who could not work out what they were used for. Experts now think that *Mononykus* evolved from a bird that could fly, but had adapted to a life in which ostrich-like legs for running after prey were more use than wings. Over time its wings had turned into stubby 'arms'.

HOW BIG WAS IT?

Did You Know?

● Experts currently place *Mononykus* in a family of early flightless birds called the Alvarezsauridae, which contains similar specimens from the late Cretaceous found in Argentina.

● Some scientists have suggested that *Mononykus* lived a mole-like existence in burrows, but although its 'arms' appear well suited to digging, its long legs would not have allowed it to excavate tunnels.

● The first *Mononykus* specimen was found in 1923 on an expedition led by US fossil hunter Roy Chapman Andrews. But the bones lay unnamed and unstudied in the American Museum of Natural History in New York until 1993, when members of another US expedition discovered three more specimens.

1 Fast and keen-eyed, an adult *Mononykus* plucks a plump lizard from the ground and drops it, still wriggling, in front of its fascinated offspring.

2 As the startled lizard runs off a young *Mononykus* gives chase, and after several clumsy strikes manages to catch the creature.

3 After a while, though, the youngster is big enough to fend for itself, and the adult drives it away to establish its own territory. From now on, the young *Mononykus* is on its own.

DINO FACTS

LENGTH	About 1m from the tip of the beaked snout to the end of the long tail
DIET	Probably insects, lizards and small mammals, and maybe some plant material
MEANING OF NAME	'Single claw'

Four incomplete specimens of *Mononykus* remains have been found, in the Bugin Tsav region of the Gobi Desert in southern Mongolia. Their bones were preserved in sand, suggesting they died in a sandstorm or collapsing dune.

MOSASAUR

FLIPPERS

A mosasaur's paddle-like flippers could be used for steering and other controlled movements.

TAIL

The long tail was flattened from side to side, like that of a fish, and in some species at least it bore vertical fins.

JAWS

A special hinge in the lower jaw allowed the mosasaur to saw large prey into chunks.

FORELIMBS

These flippers were useful for fine manoeuvres in the water. They were longer than the hindlimbs.

BODY

This was streamlined for slipping smoothly through water; it may have had a scaly skin, like that of modern lizards and snakes.

When water levels rose tens of millions of years ago, shallow seas invaded the land. In their sunlit waters roamed the largest lizards ever to have lived – the mosasaurs.

With massive jaws lined with sharp teeth, mosasaurs were the deadliest predators in the seas of their day. They preyed on fish, squid and even other smaller mosasaurs. They swam after their victims like crocodiles, paddling with their powerful flippers and using their long, flattened tail to make sweeping, side-to-side movements.

Their competitors in the prehistoric seass included the fast-swimming ichthyosaurs and the mighty pliosaurs.

HOW BIG WAS IT?

DINO FACTS

LENGTH	4–10m
WEIGHT	Up to 1 tonne
PREY	Fish, squid, other shellfish, large sea reptiles and other mosasaurs
MEANING OF NAME	'Meuse lizard', named after the river in the Netherlands where the first mosasaur fossils were found

Fossil remains of mosasaurs have been found worldwide. This map shows the shallow continental seas where they ruled supreme. Ocean water levels have dropped since, and these shallow seas have become areas of dry land.

1 The reptiles known as ichthyosaurs ruled the oceans for over 100 million years during the Triassic and Jurassic periods. They were very fast, preying on fish and squid.

2 Pliosaurs were the mosasaurs' chief rivals. With strong jaws full of sharp teeth, they killed plesiosaurs, sharks, mosasaurs, ichthyosaurs and giant squid. The jaws of *Kronosaurus* (left) measured almost 3m long.

3 By about 85 million years ago, mosasaurs had become the top predators in the world's shallow seas. Although other marine reptiles, such as giant crocodiles and plesiosaurs, were just as large, none was as successful as the mosasaurs.

Did You Know?

● The first mosasaur remains were found in a Dutch mine in the 18th century. Its scientific name, *Mosasaurus hoffmanni*, honours the scientist Dr C. Hoffman, who paid miners to chip the fossil out of rock and bring it to the surface.

● Mosasaur teeth and skeletons fetch high prices among private fossil collectors. They are especially popular in Asia because of their fancied resemblance to dragons' teeth.

● Today, only a few kinds of reptiles can be found the seas, including marine turtles, sea snakes and the saltwater crocodile.

OVIRAPTOR

CREST

The crested 'helmet' may have been colourful, to serve in display. The crest is a different shape in the two species of *Oviraptor* found so far. Also, males and females had different crests.

HEAD

A short, high skull supported a powerful toothless beak. Farther back in the mouth was a pair of peg-like teeth. Perhaps these were used for crushing eggs or snail and mussel shells.

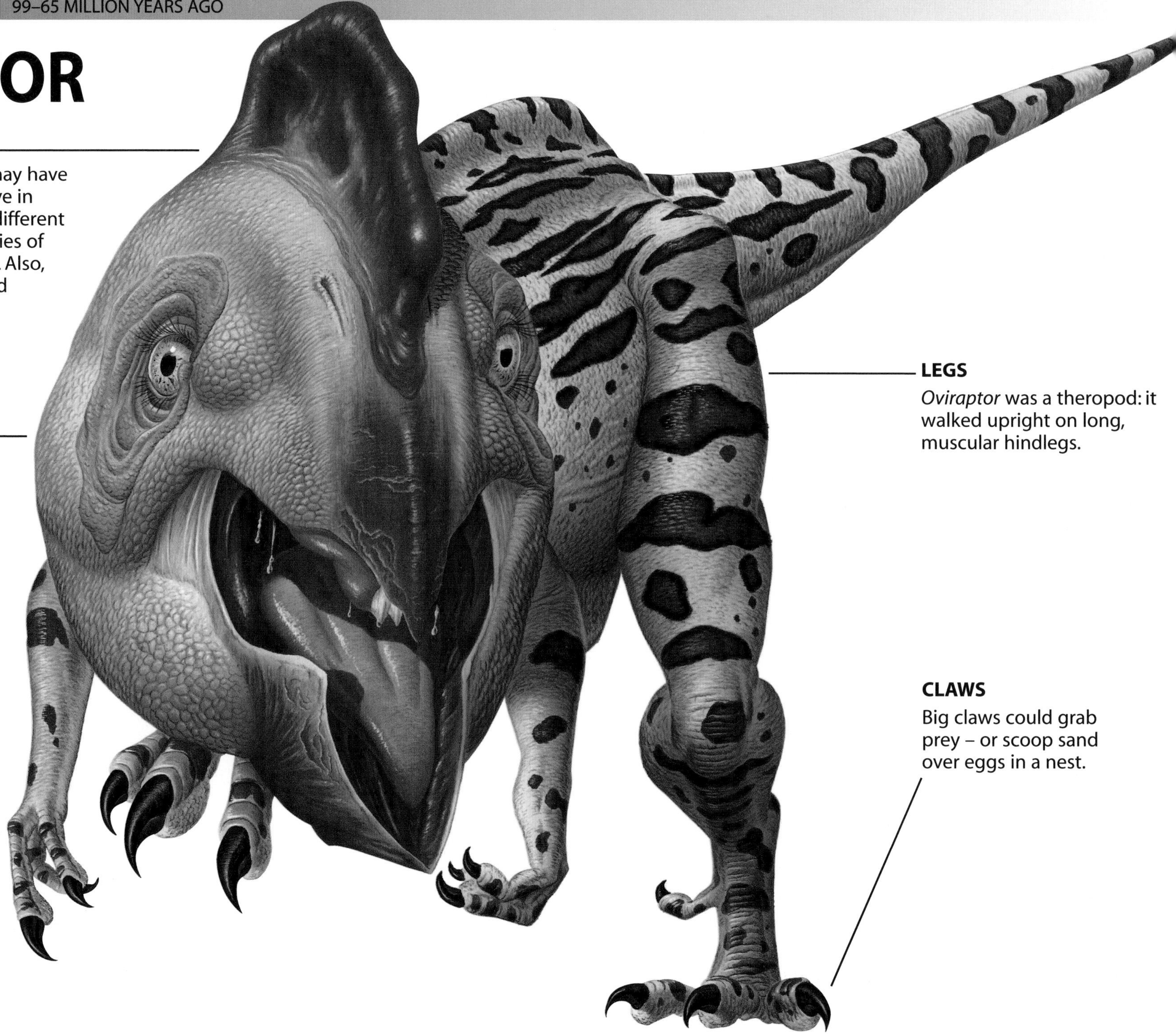

HANDS

Powerful arms ended in big hands that folded like birds' wings. A small, 'half-moon' wrist bone helped the hand move freely.

LEGS

Oviraptor was a theropod: it walked upright on long, muscular hindlegs.

CLAWS

Big claws could grab prey – or scoop sand over eggs in a nest.

For dinosaur scientists, *Oviraptor* is the subject of some of the most revealing fossil discoveries and exciting debates of recent years. The first fossil finds in the 1920s seemed to suggest that *Oviraptor* was an egg-stealing meat-eater. But beautifully preserved fossils of *Oviraptors* sitting on nests suggests that dinosaurs did not abandon their eggs to hatch without help, but kept them warm as birds do today. This evidence supports the idea that birds are modern-day dinosaurs, descended from meat-eating dinosaurs not too unlike *Oviraptor*.

The curious crest on this dinosaur's head could have been for show, for making loud noises, or for bodily functions, such as cooling the brain.

Did You Know?

● No one has yet found feathers with the *Oviraptor* skeletons, but there is evidence of feathers from its relative *Caudipteryx*, newly discovered in China. So it is possible that *Oviraptor* was feathered too. The female might have fanned the plumage around her arms as a protective 'umbrella' over the nest.

● The 'helmet' of *Oviraptor* was hollow and sponge-like on the inside, with delicate nasal passages walled with paper-thin bone. These may have helped warm and moisten the air that the dinosaur breathed. Or they may have boosted its sense of smell, or cooled its brain.

● *Oviraptor's* brain would have been large for a dinosaur, roughly as big as that of a modern flightless bird such as an ostrich or emu.

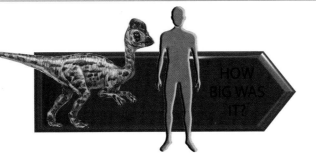

HOW BIG WAS IT?

Recent finds of fossil *Oviraptors* sitting on eggs containing baby *Oviraptors* shatter the old belief that this dinosaur stole the eggs of others. We now think it cared for its young, like modern birds. Here a mother *Oviraptor* gently turns her eggs.

DINO FACTS

LENGTH	2m
WEIGHT	60–100kg
DIET	Considered a meat-eating dinosaur, but it might have eaten anything
MEANING OF NAME	'Egg thief'

Oviraptor itself is known only from Mongolia, where several fossil skeletons have been found. Recently, scientists claim to have found *Oviraptor*-like backbones in the Americas. If they prove to be correct, then *Oviraptor* may well have lived all over the world.

1

2 The weather suddenly turns nasty. Like a roosting bird, *Oviraptor* squats dutifully over her eggs to protect them from stormy wind, rain and sand. She must not let them cool, or the babies will die.

3 Defiantly she keeps to her post, but the harsh forces of nature are too strong. Sandy drifts pile up and choke her last gasping breaths. Finally a landslide of wet sand puts her out of her misery – and preserves her, to be found millions of years later by scientists.

PACHYCEPHALOSAURUS

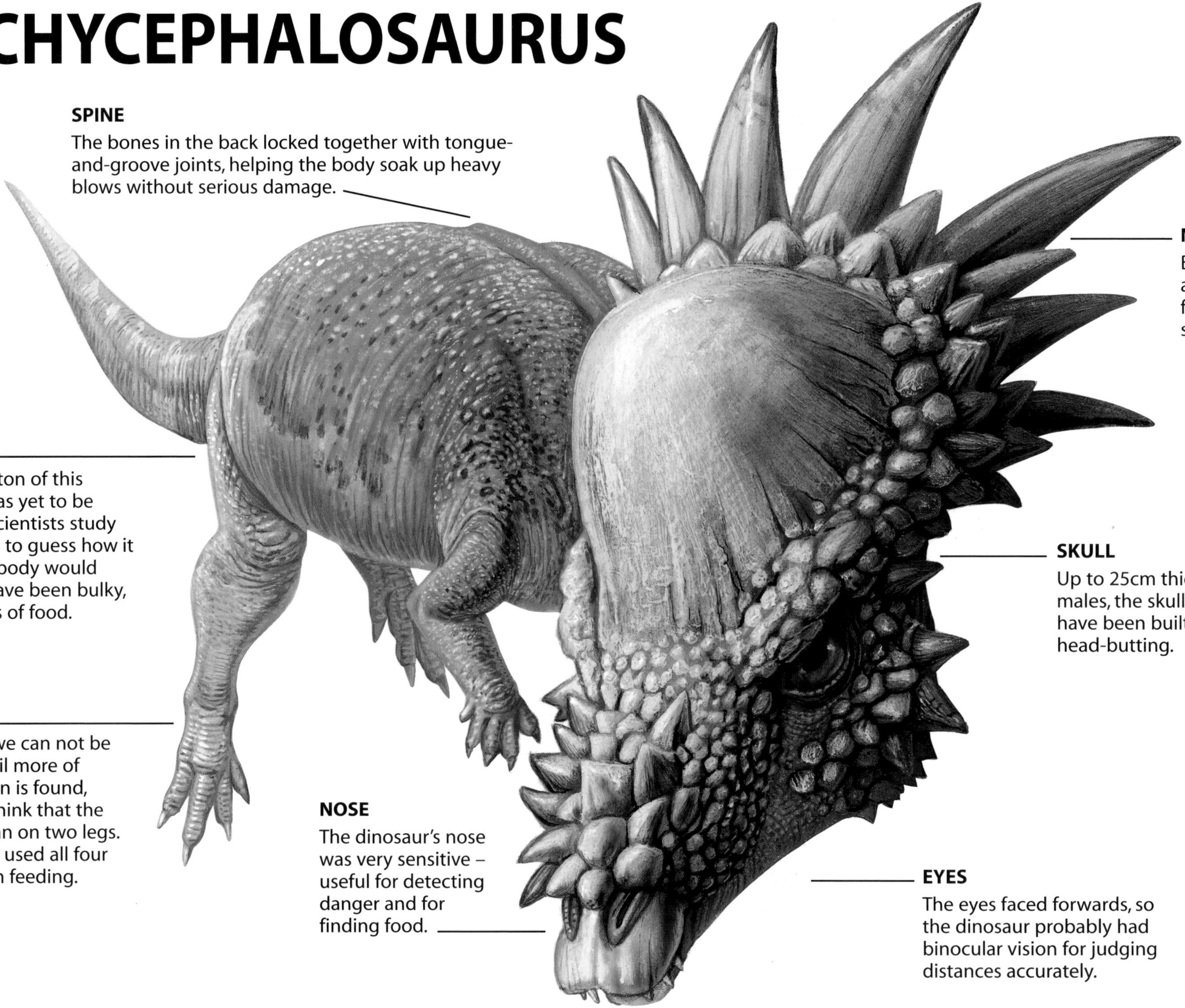

SPINE

The bones in the back locked together with tongue-and-groove joints, helping the body soak up heavy blows without serious damage.

NODULES

Bony nodules and spikes fringed the skull.

BODY

A full skeleton of this dinosaur has yet to be found, so scientists study its relatives to guess how it looked. Its body would certainly have been bulky, to hold lots of food.

SKULL

Up to 25cm thick in males, the skull may have been built for head-butting.

LEGS

Although we can not be certain until more of the skeleton is found, scientists think that the dinosaur ran on two legs. It probably used all four limbs when feeding.

NOSE

The dinosaur's nose was very sensitive – useful for detecting danger and for finding food.

EYES

The eyes faced forwards, so the dinosaur probably had binocular vision for judging distances accurately.

Males may have crashed head to head, like sheep and goats do today. The dinosaurs may have reared up and crashed down, or collided head-on from a running start.

1 ▶

Some scientists see it differently. They point out that the rounded skullcaps would have glanced off one another. Instead, these experts think the males butted one another's sides. We may never know for sure.

2 ▶

DINO FACTS

LENGTH	Up to 8m	
HEIGHT	3m at hip;, 6m at head	
WEIGHT	Up to 3 tonnes	*Pachycephalosaurus* was discovered in 1938 in Montana, USA. Since then, a few fossil bits and pieces have turned up in other nearby states. Other thick-headed dinosaurs lived in Canada, England, Mongolia, China and even Madagascar.
DIET	Plants	
MEANING OF NAME	'Thick-headed lizard'	

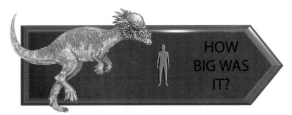

HOW BIG WAS IT?

Did You Know?

● So far, 13 kinds of 'thick-headed' dinosaur, or *pachycephalosaur*, are known. The other 12 were all much smaller than *Pachycephalosaurus*. Pachycephalosaur remains have been found in North America, England, east Asia and Madagascar.

● Pachycephalosaurs, including probably *Pachycephalosaurus* itself, had extra 'ribs' on the first 10 or so of their tail bones. This made the area behind their hips much wider than in any other two-legged dinosaurs. It just may have been an adaptation to enable them to give birth to well-developed live young.

● The famous American fossil hunter Barnum Brown discovered *Pachycephalosaurus*. Over the years he named a total of 14 dinosaurs, including the tank-like *Ankylosaurus*.

P*achycephalosaurus* was a huge animal with an immensely thick scullcap of bone adorned with clusters of mean-looking spikes. Scientists believe that this dinosaur head-butted others of its kind to win the right to mate and to gain dominance. Despite its size and scary appearance, it was probably relatively harmless. When not fighting its rivals, it most likely led a peaceful life, wandering in small herds and feeding on young leaves and other soft plant matter.

PARASAUROLOPHUS

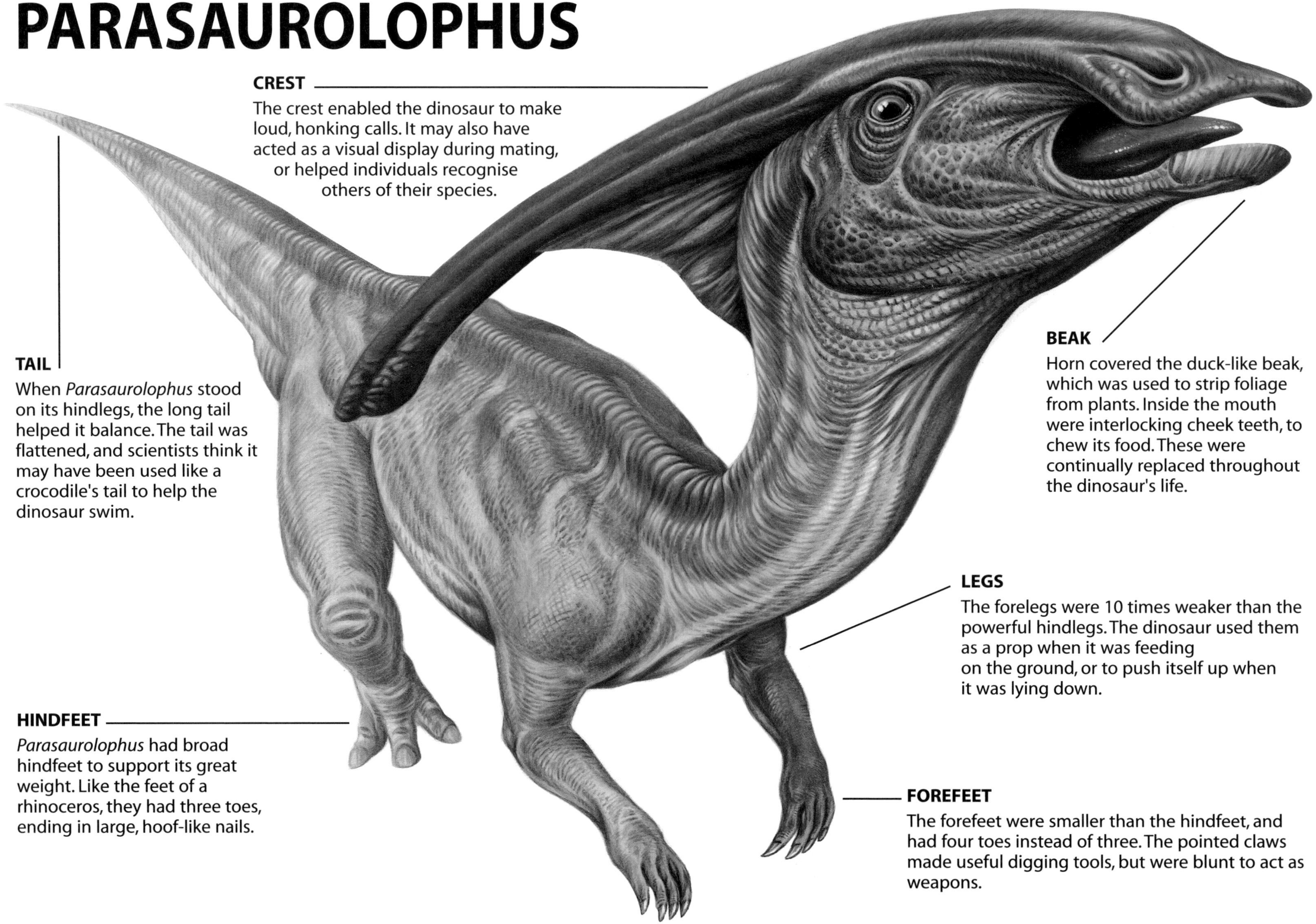

CREST

The crest enabled the dinosaur to make loud, honking calls. It may also have acted as a visual display during mating, or helped individuals recognise others of their species.

TAIL

When *Parasaurolophus* stood on its hindlegs, the long tail helped it balance. The tail was flattened, and scientists think it may have been used like a crocodile's tail to help the dinosaur swim.

BEAK

Horn covered the duck-like beak, which was used to strip foliage from plants. Inside the mouth were interlocking cheek teeth, to chew its food. These were continually replaced throughout the dinosaur's life.

LEGS

The forelegs were 10 times weaker than the powerful hindlegs. The dinosaur used them as a prop when it was feeding on the ground, or to push itself up when it was lying down.

HINDFEET

Parasaurolophus had broad hindfeet to support its great weight. Like the feet of a rhinoceros, they had three toes, ending in large, hoof-like nails.

FOREFEET

The forefeet were smaller than the hindfeet, and had four toes instead of three. The pointed claws made useful digging tools, but were blunt to act as weapons.

HOW
BIG WAS
IT?

With a tail like a crocodile, a bill like a duck and a crest on its head that doubled as a wind instrument, *Parasaurolophus* was certainly one of the strangest-looking dinosaurs of all.

This giant plant-eater may have looked like a monster, but in fact it travelled in herds of thousands as a defence against savage predatory dinosaurs.

It communicated by producing a low, booming sound. The boom may have been used both as a warning sound and during courtship. The males probably had longer crests, as they would have used them in competitive displays to impress mates.

DINO FACTS

LENGTH	10m	
HEIGHT	3m at the hip; 5.2m at the peak of the crest	
WEIGHT	3.5 tonnes	
DIET	Plants and leaves	
MEANING OF NAME	'Parallel-crested dinosaur'	

Parasaurolophus walkeri was discovered in Alberta, Canada (1), in 1920. *Parasaurolophus tubicen* and *Parasaurolophus cyrtocrystatus* were found in New Mexico, USA (2). Other specimens have since been discovered in Utah, USA (3).

Parasaurolophus tubicen had the most spectacular crest of the three species. Reaching a full metre from the back of the head, the crest would have produced a deeper note than those of the other two species.

1

Did You Know?

● In 1997, scientists in New Mexico used X-rays of a fossilized skull and computer-generated sound technology to re-create the noise *Parasaurolophus* might have made. As predicted, the sound was a deep, resonant honk.

● Although *Parasaurolophus* was huge, it was only medium-sized for a duck-billed dinosaur. The largest species, *Shantungosaurus,* grew to more than 13m long.

● Relatively little is understood about *Parasaurolophus.* Only six skulls – none of them complete – have been uncovered.

2

Parasaurolophus cyrtocrystatus had a much shorter crest than the other two species. The crest curved sharply, and would have produced the highest-pitched note. A few researchers think this was actually the female form of *Parasaurolophus*, and not a separate species at all.

3

Parasaurolophus walkeri was the first species discovered. Found in 1920, its extraordinary headgear astounded the scientific community.

PROTOCERATOPS

FRILL

To reduce weight, struts of bone rather than solid bone supported the neck frill. The male had a more upright frill than the female, perhaps to impress mates.

TAIL

The long tail shows the dinosaur's ancestors walked on two legs: a long tail acts as a balancing rod when doing this.

LEGS

All the legs were sturdily built, but the forelegs were shorter than the hindlegs.

EYES

Many experts think that the dinosaur had poor eyesight except at close quarters: like rhinoceroes today.

BEAK

The narrow, hooked beak had a horny sheath like that of a bird or a turtle.

TEETH

Shearing teeth grew from the jaws in rows. As they grew and became blunt from constant use, the old teeth fell out to reveal sharp new replacement ones.

One of the ancestors of hefty-horned dinosaurs such as the mighty *Triceratops*, this small, strangely beaked beast with its elaborate neck frill seems to have lived peacefully in herds, much like modern sheep.

The weight of its head forced *Protoceratops* to walk on four legs. This means that it would not have been able to outrun speedy killers such as *Velociraptor*, so if attacked it most probably stood its ground and defended itself with sheer brute strength and weight of numbers.

HOW BIG WAS IT?

Two marauding *Velociraptors* charge towards a herd of *Protoceratops*, intent on devouring one of their babies. The adult *Protoceratops* bunch together around their young.

1

Desperately hungry, the *Velociraptors* persist with their attack. Suddenly one gets too close – and a furious *Protoceratops* tears into it, ripping flesh and crushing bone.

2

DINO FACTS

LENGTH	Up to 2.5r
HEIGHT	Up to 75c at the hip
WEIGHT	Probably to 260kg
DIET	Low-growing plants
MEANING OF NAME	'First horn-face'

Protoceratops fossils were first discovered in the 1920s, in the Gobi Desert in Mongolia. The dinosaur is also known from finds in North America, which was joined to Asia when *Protoceratops* was alive.

Did You Know?

● *Protoceratops* was discovered in 1922, when the American Museum of Natural History sent a team to the Gobi Desert in Mongolia to search for ancient human remains. On this and later expeditions to the Gobi Desert in the 1920s, teams led by Roy Chapman Andrews found more than 100 *Protoceratops* skeletons. Some were in death poses, on their backs with their feet to the sky.

● A Polish team of experts made a remarkable find in Mongolia in the 1960s: a *Protoceratops* grappling with a *Velociraptor*, a vicious meat-eating dinosaur. The battling beasts died in a landslide or sandstorm.

● An expedition to Mongolia in 1994 found the fossil remains of a few tiny hatchling *Protoceratops* with skulls less than 3cm long.

PTERANODON

CREST
The long crest may have balanced the heavy bill as *Pteranodon* scooped fish from the sea. It may also have worked as a rudder for steering in flight.

MEMBRANE
Like the wings of a bat, the wings of *Pteranodon* were made from light, flexible and strong skin. Each wing stretched from the long fourth finger at the front to the upper hindleg at the rear.

BODY
Some experts think *Pteranodon* had oily, feather-like hair to keep it warm and dry. No one really knows because any fur would have rotted away long before the animal's bones started to fossilize.

EYES
The large eyes faced forwards for binocular vision – essential for judging distance.

WINGS
Each thin wing was held up by the forelimb and a long fourth finger.

BILL
Like a pelican, *Pteranodon* may have had a large, drooping pouch below its bill in which to store fish.

One of the largest of all the flying reptiles discovered so far, *Pteranodon* soared across the North American skies looking like a cross between a giant bat and a large pelican. It had the wingspan of a small plane and yet weighed no more than a large turkey.

Pteranodon lived alongside a landlocked ocean, probably in clifftop colonies, from which it could launch itself on marathon fishing expeditions.

There were many kinds of flying reptiles. Early ones were small, with teeth to eat insects and fish. Later ones were huge, with toothless or bristle-lined bills.

Eudimorphodon was one of the first flying reptiles. An almost perfect fossil was found in Triassic rocks in the Italian Alps. *Eudimorphodon* was as big as a gull, with a long neck, large head and pointed jaws. It probably ate fish – its teeth are much like those of fish-eating seals.

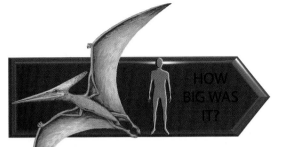

HOW BIG WAS IT?

DINO FACTS

WINGSPAN	Up to 9m, depending on species and sex (female two-thirds that of male)	
WEIGHT	Up to 20kg, depending on species and sex	Most *Pteranodon* fossils come from an area of Kansas in the USA that is part of the Niobrara Formation, a limestone deposit that was once the floor of an inland ocean. Fossil hunters found the first bone fragments in the 1860s, at a site on the Smoky Hill River.
LENGTH OF SKULL	Up to 1.8m, depending on sex and species (females had smaller crests)	
DIET	Fish	
MEANING OF NAME	'Winged, – without teeth'	

1

Pteranodon had a long, thin, toothless, upward-curving bill. Skimming the waves, it would have dipped its bill into the sea to catch fish. The sharp edges of the bill could have cut up large fish. *Pteranodon* may have stored small fish in a pouch before swallowing them.

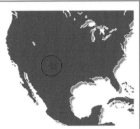

Did You Know?

● The female *Pteranodon* had a wider pelvis than the male, most likely to allow her to lay big eggs.

● Early flying reptiles had a long tail, tipped with a diamond-shaped, rudder-like vane – perhaps to help them make tight twists and turns when chasing flying insects.

● Fossils of food pellets coughed up by prehistoric fish have been found that contain bones of an early flying reptile, *Preondactylus*. This may mean some flying reptiles occasionally crashed into the sea, or were sometimes grabbed by fish as they swooped over the waves.

2

Pterodaustro was a South American flying reptile that lived in the early Cretaceous period. It had a long, upward-curving bill. Its lower jaw was lined with 400–500 bristles. *Pterodaustro* probably scooped up water and squeezed it out through the bristles, to trap tiny shrimps and other small animals.

3

QUETZALCOATLUS

NECK

Estimated at 2.4m long, the neck would have been strengthened by tendons and muscles fixed to the shoulders, to keep it rigid and streamlined in flight.

WINGS

A light and flexible but strong layer of skin would have covered the bones of each wing. On the ground, the creature would have folded its wings out of the way, much as a bird does.

EYES

Large eyes giving good distance vision are essential for any creature that spots prey from high in the air.

BONES

The bones of flying reptiles were hollow, for lightness.

CLAWS

Long claws would have helped the flying reptile cling to rocks when roosting after a long flight.

NOSTRILS

These would have been set high on the head so that they did not fill with water when the reptile plunged its bill into a river or lake.

BODY

Flying reptiles had a slim, streamlined body design – one that was light and aerodynamic.

BILL

A long, toothless bill with sharp edges is ideal for snapping up slippery fish.

With a wingspan of around 11–12m, *Quetzalcoatlus* may well have been the largest creature ever to take to the air. This incredible flying reptile could have stayed airborne for hours as it scanned the surface of rivers and lakes for fish to scoop up in its massive, toothless bill. As with other flying reptiles, its wings would have been attached to the top of its legs only, so some experts think that it may have walked upright with its wings folded. It may even have run along the ground to launch itself into the air, much as an albatross does.

Only a very few wing–bone fossils have ever been found, but smaller, more complete fossils may be the remains of young.

HOW BIG WAS IT?

A young *Quetzalcoatlus* launches itself into the air, eager to join its fellow fliers in the sky. Straining its powerful flight muscles to the limit, the reptile accelerates from take-off to cruising speed in around 20 wingbeats.

1

DINO FACTS

LENGTH	Up to 6m, including bill and 2.4m neck	The wing bones of *Q. northropi* were found in 1971 in Big Bend National Park, Texas, USA. More complete fossils of smaller but similar creatures have since been found there and in Alberta, Canada. These are the remains either of smaller *Quetzalcoatlus* species, or of juvenile specimens of *Q. northropi*.
WINGSPAN	Probably 11–12m	
WEIGHT	Estimated at 80–90kg	
PREY	Freshwater fish and crustaceans	
MEANING OF NAME	'Like Quetzalcoatl' (the snake god of the Aztec people)	

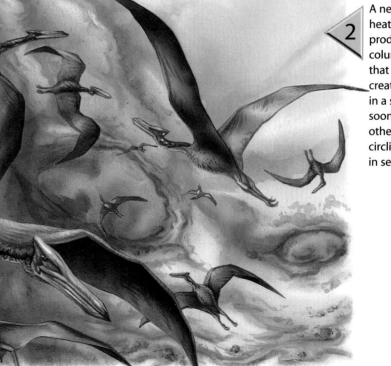

2 A nearby hill, heated by the sun, produces a warm column of rising air that lifts the creature upwards in a slow spiral. It soon joins the other reptiles circling over pools in search of fish.

Did You Know?

● In 1976, in Texas, there was a wave of sightings of giant, flying reptiles just like *Quetzalcoatlus*. Reports came from police officers and teachers, among others. After two months, the reports stopped as suddenly as they had begun.

● So far, more than 100 species of prehistoric flying reptile have been discovered. They range in size from *Quetzalcoatlus* down to *Sordes*, which was no bigger than a pigeon.

● Some experts speculate that prehistoric flying reptiles such as *Quetzalcoatlus* nested in large colonies, as many birds do today.

SALTASAURUS

ARMOUR
Thick, ridged plating and rough nodules spread across the back of *Saltasaurus* would have kept the animal safe from most predators.

HEAD
No complete *Saltasaurus* skull has been found, but many scientists think that its head would have been similar to that of another sauropod, *Diplodocus*.

TEETH
Saltasaurus, like other sauropods, probably had long, peg-like teeth to strip leaves off branches.

TAIL
The tail bones were linked by ball-and-socket joints for strength with flexibility.

FRONT FEET
The front feet, undiscovered so far, may have had a thumb-like digit that was armed with a sharp claw – like those on its relatives.

This colossal plant-eater had a coat of bony plates and nodules on its back and sides that made it a daunting target for even the deadliest predators. Together the plates and nodules acted rather like the chain-mail shirts worn by medieval knights.

Saltosaurus lived in South America about 75 million years ago. It was a member of a group of giant, long-necked dinosaurs called sauropods. Some were so massive they made the ground quake as they walked.

Saltosaurus had a long, sturdy tail that supported its weight as the mighty leaf-eater reared up to feed on foliage high up in the trees.

HOW BIG WAS IT?

DINO FACTS

LENGTH	12m	So far *Saltasaurus'* distinctive fossil remains have been recovered only from Argentina and Uruguay, in South America. Scientists suggest that unusual sauropods such as *Saltasaurus* may have developed into unique forms because South America was surrounded by water and isolated from North America.
WEIGHT	Possibly up to 10 tonnes	
DIET	Plants — probably ferns and tree foliage	
MEANING OF NAME	'Salta lizard' (Salta is the Argentine province where its fossils were first found)	

A savage *Giganotosaurus* spots a lone *Saltasaurus* on its hindlegs, browsing the high foliage of a coniferous tree. With a great roar, the killer rushes over to attack.

1

Did You Know?

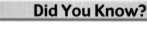

● *Saltasaurus* was not the only armoured sauropod. The fossils of *Laplatosaurus*, another long-necked plant-eater from South America, show a similar protective covering.

● Some scientists believe that sauropods used their long tails as weapons, to inflict stinging blows on their enemies, and to communicate with other members of a herd, by using booming whip-crack sounds.

● *Saltasaurus* was first found in 1893, but it was not until 100 years later that it was correctly identified as a sauropod. Fossil hunters were mystified by the discovery of bony plates and bumps among its fossil remains. This form of armour had previously only been seen among the fossils of ankylosaurs – smaller dinosaurs unrelated to sauropods.

2

Alarmed by the noise, the plant-eater crouches with only its armoured back and sides exposed. The hapless predator breaks claws and teeth in a vain attempt to breach the creature's defences.

STYRACOSAURUS

HORNS
The nose horn and other spikes each had a bony core under layers of keratin, the fibrous material in hair, feathers, claws, hoofs, horns and fingernails.

BODY
The dinosaur's great girth allowed plenty of room inside for a long gut. This is essential if you eat vast quantities of coarse plants that take a long time to digest.

SPIKY FRILL
A bony extension of the skull, this protected the animal's neck. Two large holes in the bone, covered by skin, lessened its weight.

FEET
These were broad to spread the load that they bore.

LEGS
The legs were thick and sturdy. The hindlegs were longer than the forelegs, giving the dinosaur a slightly sloping profile.

BEAK
Styracosaurus had a horny beak for shearing off great mouthfuls of tough vegetation. It could not chew, but ground its food into a pulp with teeth in the back of its mouth.

This awesome dinosaur was more than adequately equipped to defend itself against the meanest and mightiest predators. *Styracosaurus* sported a huge nose horn and a spiky headdress, and would have stood no nonsense from vicious meat-eaters. It probably charged headfirst into the attack, using its nose horn as a lethal weapon to gore its rival.

Experts think that *Styracosaurus* lived in small family groups. In each group there may have been a dominant adult male, several adult females and a number of young males and females.

SPIKY SURPRISE

A *Styracosaurus* browses on the edge of a forest, unaware it is being watched. Suddenly, a *Tyrannosaurus rex* pounds out of the trees. It hesitates at the sight of the *Styracosaurus'* spiky headgear and then tries a lunging overhead bite. In that moment, *Styracosaurus* thrusts its long nose horn deep into the hunter's exposed belly.

Did You Know?

● *Styracosaurus* was discovered in 1913, when an expedition of the Geological Survey of Canada found an almost complete skull at a site on the Red Deer River in Alberta. Only part of the bony core of the nose horn is missing.

● *Styracosaurus'* nose horn was the longest of any known dinosaur. Experts estimate that it grew up to 1m long – maybe even more.

● When *Styracosaurus* hatched, it had no nose horn or spikes at all. They only grew gradually as the dinosaur got older – as is the case with horned mammals today.

● *Styracosaurus* was one of the last ever dinosaurs. It perished, along with all the other dinosaurs living at the time, some 65 million years ago.

HOW BIG WAS IT?

DINO FACTS

LENGTH	5.5m
HEIGHT	2m at hip; 1.5m at head
WEIGHT	2.5 tonnes
DIET	Plants
MEANING OF NAME	'Spike lizard'

Styracosaurus is known from two sites: one in Alberta (1) in Canada, and the other in Montana (2) in the USA. When it was alive, a shallow sea divided North America down the middle. *Styracosaurus* lived on the western side of that divide.

TYRANNOSAURUS REX

HEAD
T. rex probably charged big prey at full speed, its jaws agape. This would have inflicted maximum injury and reduced the risk of a struggle.

TAIL
This may have acted as a stiff counterbalance to the *T. rex's* heavy body, like the tail of a kangaroo.

LEGS
Strong thigh muscles helped support the dinosaur's weight and could have provided the power for sprinting.

FORELIMBS
Experts have long puzzled over these. They were too short to reach the mouth and had only two 'fingers', each armed with a stout claw.

TEETH
Worked by crushingly powerful jaws, the saw-blade teeth would have sliced skin and crunched bone with ease. Most likely, *T. rex* gulped down great mouthfuls of flesh and bone, like a crocodile.

One of the largest and most terrifying creatures the world has known, *Tyrannosaurus rex* once lived in what is now North America. It was so immensely strong it would have been able to overpower almost any other animal of its day. Its huge jaws were filled with around 50 dagger-like teeth that could have ripped prey apart with one or two deadly bites.

In the past, most experts believed that *T. rex* just plodded about, but scientists now believe that it could have raced along, holding its tail off the ground. They have based their theories on the way certain animals run today, such as the ostrich and the crocodile.

HOW BIG WAS IT?

DINO FACTS

LENGTH	Up to 12m
WEIGHT	Probably about 7 tonnes
DIET	Reptiles, and other dinosaurs, dead or alive
MEANING OF NAME	'King tyrant lizard'

Fossil *T. rex* bones have been found in the states of Wyoming (1), South Dakota (2) and Montana (3) – but no complete skeleton has ever been found. Famous fossil hunter Barnum Brown found the first, at the start of the 20th century. The recent find was in Montana in 1997.

OSTRICH

Modern birds may well be the direct descendants of some dinosaurs. They have an upright, or 'improved', stance, like *T. rex*. This means they are highly mobile on the ground. Some birds, such as the ostrich, have superb sprinting abilities.

1

2 CROCODILE

The crocodile has a 'semi-improved' stance. Unlike lizards, which have a 'sprawling' stance, a crocodile can lift its body on its half-straight legs. But crocodiles and lizards can run only in short bursts.

Did You Know?

● Although *T. rex* had a small brain for such a big animal, it was probably no less intelligent than a crocodile. Some crocodiles occasionally hunt in packs, so perhaps *T. rex* did the same.

● The skin of *T. rex* was almost certainly covered in scales, like that of a lizard. The dinosaur may have been brightly coloured to attract a mate, or camouflaged for ambushing prey.

● One *T. rex* found has the tooth of another *T. rex* embedded in its neck.

● Skulls of even bigger meat-eating dinosaurs than *T. rex* have been found in Argentina and Africa: *Giganotosaurus* and *Carcharodontosaurus*.

3

TYRANNOSAURUS REX

Like all dinosaurs, birds and mammals, *T. rex* had a 'fully improved' stance: its body was supported on straight legs. This may have been the key to the dinosaur's success, as it probably meant *T. rex* could run at speed for some distance.

TARBOSAURUS

TEETH

These would have inflicted hideous, gaping wounds, often delivering a quick kill, and also doubled as efficient butchery tools.

JAWS

The heavily muscled jaws designed to open wide to take a massive bite.

HEAD

The size of the head and the thickness of its skull shows it probably attacked like a battering ram. The skull bones had flexible joints that would have helped absorb the shock of impact.

FORELIMBS

These puny forelimbs were of little use as weapons. They probably reduced in size, as *Tarbosaurus* relied increasingly on two-legged speed and the power of its jaws.

*T*arbosaurus was one of the deadliest hunters of its age, with the speed and strength to tackle the biggest and fastest prey. It probably waited in ambush and caught its victims in a final charging rush. Slamming into its prey, *Tarbosaurus* flung its jaws wide open, inflicting huge bites, while its teeth ripped through the flesh with ease.

It is clear from a study of its skeleton that *Tarbosaurus* was built to deal with heavyweight victims. The thickness of its skull bones and its bulky neck and upper spine would have cushioned the force of its battering-ram attack. Huge muscles and powerful legs and tail provided the strength and agility for a lightning charge.

HOW BIG WAS IT?

Did You Know?

● A Russian scientific expedition to Mongolia in 1948–49 uncovered the remains of seven skeletons of *Tarbosaurus* juveniles and adults.

● *Tarbosaurus* prowled around Asia at a time when another huge killer, *Tyrannosaurus rex*, reigned in North America. Some scientists think that, in spite of slight differences in size and skull formation, *Tarbosaurus* and *T. rex* belong to the same genus. The Mongolian predator is probably the more ancient of the two reptiles. *T. rex* may have crossed to North America via a land bridge from Asia.

● No one knows how *Tarbosaurus* used its tiny forelimbs. They may have helped it push itself up off the ground, or perhaps the male used them to grip a female when mating.

1 A grazing *Gallimimus* group keeps a constant lookout for predators, but *Tarbosaurus* edges ever closer until the prey are within range of its short, devastating sprint.

2 The killer commits everything to a single headlong charge. With deadly jaws open wide, it bulldozes one panic-stricken plant-eater flat – then starts to feed greedily on its bloody flesh.

DINO FACTS

LENGTH	8.5–13m, including 1.5m skull
HEIGHT	Up to 6m
WEIGHT	Up to 6 tonnes
DIET	Other dinosaurs
WEAPONS	Sharp, serrated teeth
MEANING OF NAME	'Alarming lizard'

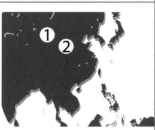

Scientists found the first *Tarbosaurus* fossils in southern Mongolia, in the Nemegt Basin region of the Gobi Desert (1). Later, further remains surfaced in the Xixia Basin of Henan Province, China (2).

TRICERATOPS

TAIL

Held out behind its rump, the long, stout tail acted as a counterbalance for the heavy head.

HORNS

A *Triceratops* did not have horns at birth, but grew them as it reached adulthood.

HIND LEGS

Triceratops had pillar-like legs, a bit like those of an elephant, to support its huge bulk. It probably moved no faster than 4km/h, but then this mighty beast seldom had to run away.

FORELEGS

In *Triceratops*, the upper foreleg bone is a peculiar shape. It seems that, unusually for a dinosaur, the animal may have had slightly bow-legged forelimbs.

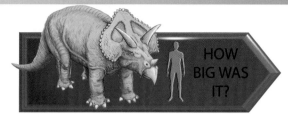

Weighing as much as a small car and with a mighty, helmet-like head bristling with horns, *Triceratops* was a giant among dinosaurs. Few predators would have dared to pick a fight with it.

On some adults the eye horns grew to more than 90cm in length. *Triceratops* would have used these lethal weapons to fend off meat-eaters, such as *Tyrannosaurus rex*. Relatives of *Triceratops*, shown right, also sported magnificent head gear.

One of the biggest of all ceratopsians (horned-face dinosaurs), *Triceratops* survived up until the mass extinction of the dinosaurs, some 65 million years ago.

HOW BIG WAS IT?

DINO FACTS

LENGTH	About 9m
WEIGHT	Up to 8.5 tonnes
HEIGHT	2.2m at the hips
DIET	Foliage and woody growth of trees
MEANING OF NAME	'Bristling three-horned face'

Although hundreds of *Triceratops* fossils have been found, they are restricted to a small area of western North America, in Wyoming and Montana in the USA, and Saskatchewan and Alberta in Canada.

CENTROSAURUS

The *Centrosaurus* skull was deep and boxy, and the frill was short. This savage-looking creature had a single huge horn.

PACHYRHINOSAURUS

Pachyrhinosaurus had a very thick boss of bone and horn over the nose. It is possible that the animal used its chunky snout horn to push and shove in fights with rivals over mates.

STYRACOSAURUS

As well as a long, sword-like nose horn, *Styracosaurus* had up to six frill horns, giving it the look of a monstrous animated pineapple.

Did You Know?

● Most dinosaurs are known from only a handful of specimens, but the fossil finds of *Triceratops* include more than 50 skulls.

● One of the most dedicated collectors of *Triceratops* fossils was John Bell Hatcher. Working in Wyoming, USA, from 1888 to 1892, he gathered 33 skulls, the largest of which weighed more than 3 tonnes.

● *Triceratops* bones have been found in vast numbers in Dinosaur Provincial Park in Alberta, Canada. Scientists think that these are the remains of a huge herd, trapped trying to cross a flooding river.

● In 1994, local schoolchildren voted *Triceratops* to be the state fossil of Wyoming. It is also the state dinosaur of South Dakota.

TROÖDON

HEAD
The narrow, birdlike head held a large brain. *Troödon* had a wide range of tooth types, including the small, saw-edged blades which sliced into flesh.

FEET
Each foot had four toes. The extra-large second toe was armed with a great, sickle-shaped claw for striking killer blows.

LEGS
Powerful thighs and long, strong legs allowed speedy running.

EYES
Eyes set forward on head gave good stereoscopic vision. Their great size enabled *Troödon* to hunt in dim light or at night – a time when mammal prey would have been active.

TAIL
This was long and muscled with a whippy tip. It could be swung rapidly to aid balance as *Troödon* sprinted after prey.

HANDS
Three long, bony fingers had sharp claws used for gripping prey.

Troödon was on the small side for a dinosaur: it stood no taller than an adult man. But scientists reckon that it had the best vision of any dinosaur, enabling it to zero in on prey with deadly accuracy. It also had a relatively big brain and may have been the cleverest of the dinosaurs too.

It was able to run fast on its muscular hindlegs and probably hunted down almost anything it could tear apart with its razor-sharp teeth, bony fingers and sickle-clawed toes.

Fossils from North America show that it laid eggs and sat on them until they hatched, like birds do today.

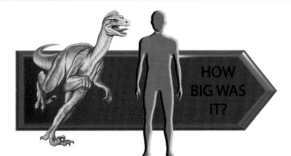

HOW BIG WAS IT?

DINO FACTS

SIZE	About 1.8m long and 80cm high
WEIGHT	About 45kg
DIET	Other dinosaurs; lizards and other reptiles; insects
MEANING OF NAME	'Wounding tooth'

Troödon lived in North America. Its fossils have been found in Montana and Wyoming, USA, and in Alberta, Canada. The remains of its closest relatives have turned up in Mongolia.

2 One or both parents sits on the eggs, just as birds do today. On hatching, each baby *Troödon* emerges fully formed, like a tiny replica of its parents.

1 The mother half-buries her eggs after laying them. This keeps them still. Like the eggs of today's reptiles, *Troödon* eggs had to be securely anchored to ensure that the babies were not born deformed.

Did You Know?

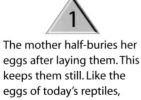

● *Troödon* eggs were big with hard shells. Large eggs take longer to hatch, and the embryos would have had more time to develop before hatching. *Troödon* babies probably popped the tops off their shells, and crawled out.

● The first fossilized dinosaur eggs were discovered in France in 1869. Since then, many egg finds have been made, at sites in the USA, Argentina, France, India, Mongolia and China.

● Many of the dinosaur eggs that are excavated still have the original shell around them. Scientists have identified amino acids (compounds that build animal protein) from them. These amino acids are remarkably similar to those found in the eggshells of birds today.

VELOCIRAPTOR

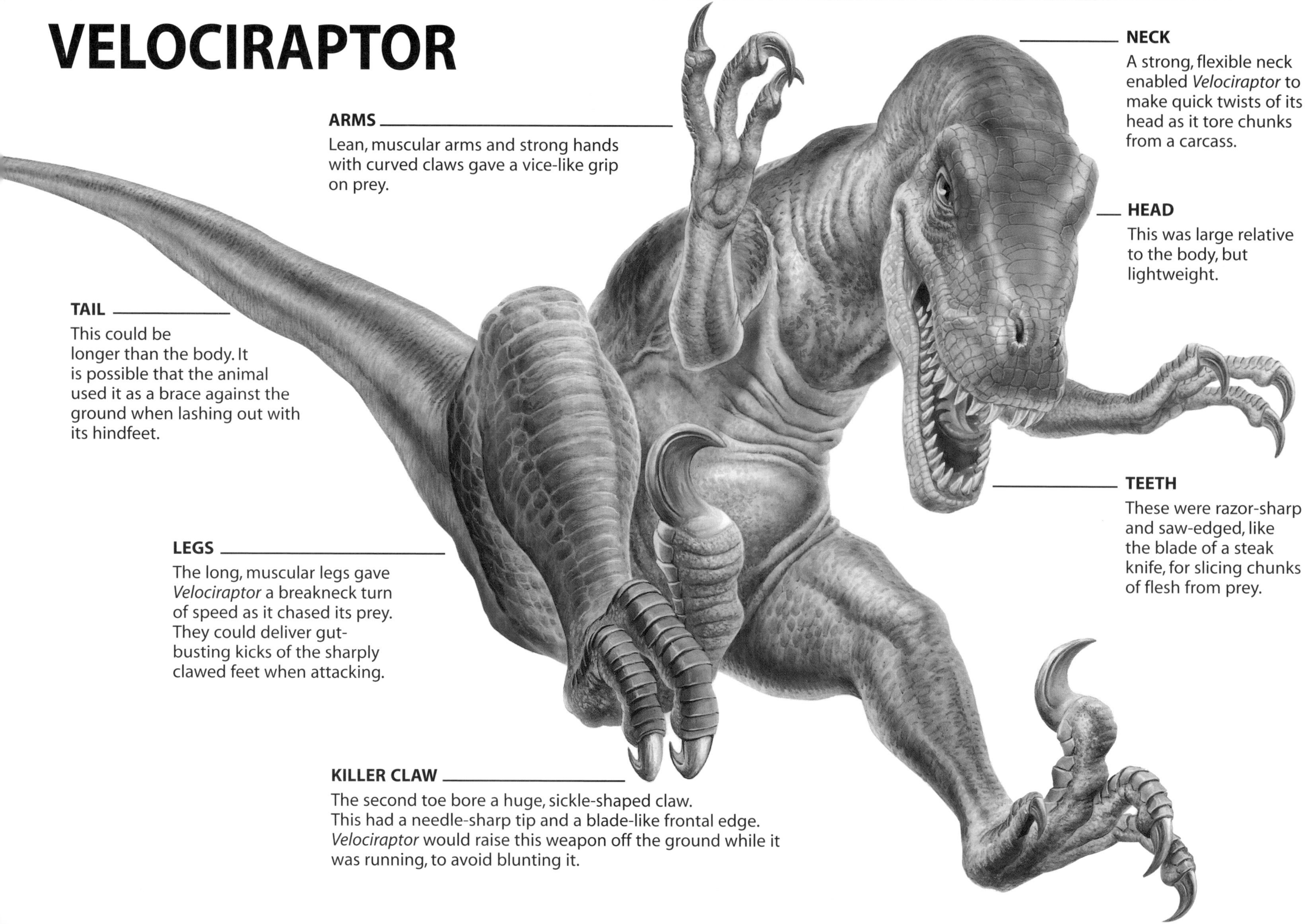

NECK

A strong, flexible neck enabled *Velociraptor* to make quick twists of its head as it tore chunks from a carcass.

ARMS

Lean, muscular arms and strong hands with curved claws gave a vice-like grip on prey.

HEAD

This was large relative to the body, but lightweight.

TAIL

This could be longer than the body. It is possible that the animal used it as a brace against the ground when lashing out with its hindfeet.

TEETH

These were razor-sharp and saw-edged, like the blade of a steak knife, for slicing chunks of flesh from prey.

LEGS

The long, muscular legs gave *Velociraptor* a breakneck turn of speed as it chased its prey. They could deliver gut-busting kicks of the sharply clawed feet when attacking.

KILLER CLAW

The second toe bore a huge, sickle-shaped claw. This had a needle-sharp tip and a blade-like frontal edge. *Velociraptor* would raise this weapon off the ground while it was running, to avoid blunting it.

Velociraptor may have stood only knee-high to its prey, but it made up for its small size with sheer ferocity. Hunting in packs, it would have been unstoppable. This small but intelligent predator roamed the hostile plains of what is now Mongolia, alongside hordes of other deadly meat-eating dinosaurs. It may have looked ungainly loping along with its sickle-shaped toes cocked back, but this kept them ready and sharp to tear apart its prey and enemies.

Fossils show that *Velociraptor* was one of the most advanced killers of its day. It had a big brain, so it was probably intelligent and alert. Its eyes were big, and its sense of smell was doubtlessly excellent.

HOW BIG WAS IT?

1 *Velociraptor* liked its steaks good 'n' rare. It probably targeted big, slow plant-eaters, tackling them in a pack, but had a go at anything – even speedy *Gallimimus* (below). First, *Velociraptor* used its keen eyesight to single out a sick, young or old animal from a herd, and gave chase. At the last minute, it lunged for the neck, grappling with foreclaws and teeth. Then it reached up with a hindfoot, flicking forwards its second toe. Easy as a scalpel, the knife-edged talon slit open its prey (detail, left).

DINO FACTS

LENGTH	About 1.8m overall, head to tail tip
WEIGHT	About 15kg
DIET	Other dinosaurs, especially slow-moving plant-eaters
MEANING OF NAME	'Speedy plunderer'

So far, fossils of *Velociraptor* have been found only in Mongolia and nearby parts of China, in Central Asia. The first discovery was made in 1923, in the Flaming Cliffs of Mongolia.

Did You Know?

● A pack of these waist-high predators could probably have ripped apart a human victim in just 30 seconds – but for the fact that *Velociraptor* has been extinct for about 70 million years.

● From examining the shape of one of its hipbones, some dinosaur scientists think that *Velociraptor* may have sat upright like a dog, rather than crouch on its belly.

● Scientists used to believe that dinosaurs relied, like modern reptiles, on the sun and other heat sources to warm up their bodies. Today, some experts think *Velociraptor* and its cousins could have been warm-blooded, like modern birds and mammals. This way, they could have lived a highly active lifestyle.

2 Even as *Gallimimus* lay panting in the dust, its life blood ebbing away, *Velociraptor* began its meal. Squatting at *Gallimimus'* ripped side, it laid in with tooth and claw, tearing out chunks of hot flesh and tossing them down its slender neck.

After the Dinosaurs

The last of the dinosaurs died out in the great extinction that came at the very end of the Cretaceous period. But other curious and remarkable prehistoric creatures survived, and these soon filled the gap left by the dinosaurs.

Whatever did kill off the dinosaurs, lots of other creatures survived and prospered. One prehistoric reptile, the crocodile, still exists today, barely changed over millions of years. The shark is another creature from the age of the dinosaurs, although modern sharks are nowhere near as big as the *Megladon*,which terrorized the oceans of this period. Among the other survivors were amphibians such as frogs and toads, and birds, which are probably descended from the flying dinosaurs such as *Archaeopteryx*. Meanwhile the warm-blooded mammals flourished and eventually developed into prehistoric beasts such as the sabre-toothed cat and the woolly mammoth.

In the period that followed the extinction of the dinosaurs, many creatures started to resemble the animals we know today. *Basilosaurus* was on the way to becoming a whale. The huge *Diatryma* looked like a pelican and *Borhyaena* like a wolf. And by the very end of the period covered in this chapter, long after the last of the dinosaurs, we find another strange mammal living among these creatures—man.

ANDREWSARCHUS

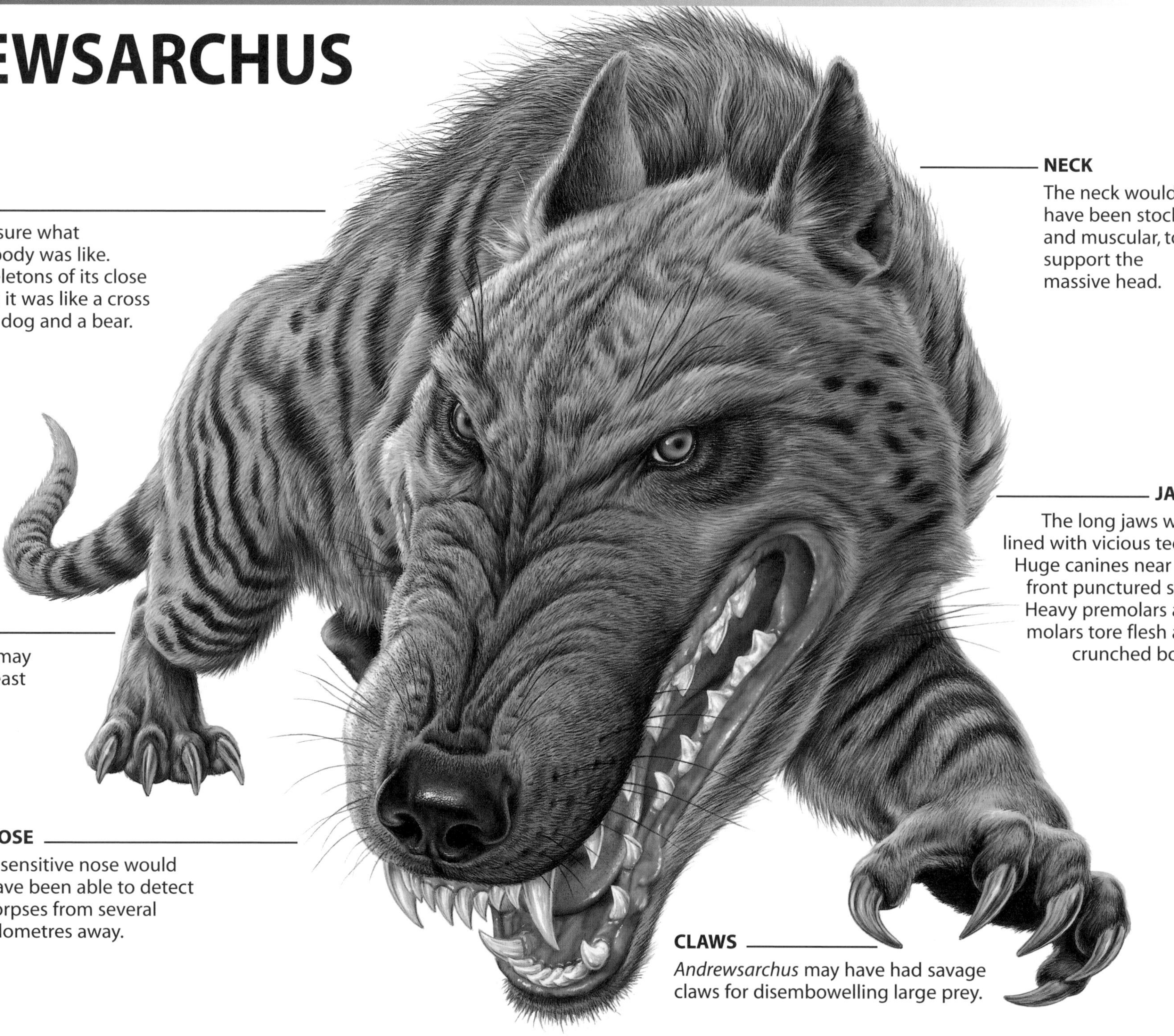

BODY

Scientists are unsure what *Andrewsarchus'* body was like. However, the skeletons of its close relatives suggest it was like a cross between a giant dog and a bear.

NECK

The neck would have been stocky and muscular, to support the massive head.

JAWS

The long jaws were lined with vicious teeth. Huge canines near the front punctured skin. Heavy premolars and molars tore flesh and crunched bone.

HINDLEGS

Powerful hindlegs may have helped the beast to run down prey.

NOSE

A sensitive nose would have been able to detect corpses from several kilometres away.

CLAWS

Andrewsarchus may have had savage claws for disembowelling large prey.

Up to six metres long and with a mouth big enough to swallow a man, this beast was truly the stuff of nightmares. *Andrewsarchus* was like a giant hyena, a specialist in seeking out the dead and the dying. It was the biggest meat-eating mammal that ever lived on land. Its massive skull had strong jaws filled with huge teeth for crunching bones.

Scientists think that it was a close relative of the most primitive whales. The earliest known whale was *Pakicetus*, which had many features in common with *Andrewsarchus*, most notably its teeth.

HOW BIG WAS IT?

DINO FACTS

LENGTH	Probably 5–6m
HEIGHT	Probably 2m at shoulder
WEIGHT	Probably over 1 tonne
DIET	Probably carcasses
MEANING OF NAME	'Andrews' ancient one'

Andrewsarchus is known from a single complete fossilized skull found in the Gobi Desert of Mongolia in 1923. No other remains have been found.

Did You Know?

● *Andrewsarchus* may be named after Roy Chapman Andrews, but its fossil skull was actually discovered by one of his assistants. The Chinese fossil expert Kan Chuen Pao, known to his colleagues as 'Buckshot', found it when the party stopped briefly at a site called Irden Mannah.

● Roy Chapman Andrews found many new prehistoric animals on his expeditions to Mongolia in the 1920s, including the dinosaurs *Oviraptor* and *Velociraptor*. He also discovered the first dinosaur eggs.

● Some scientists think that *Andrewsarchus* had hoofs, not claws. Until someone finds further fossil remains, we cannot be sure.

● Roy Chapman Andrews was nicknamed 'Gobi' on his expeditions.

FRESH FOOD
Andrewsarchus may have hunted, but it was probably mainly a scavenger. Here, the big carnivore has found an injured *Uintathere* lying helpless on the ground. The beast eats the plant-eater alive, ripping open its belly and feasting on its innards.

BASILOSAURUS

BODY
The animal's body was long and streamlined. It was packed with muscle for powering in pursuit of fresh prey.

TAIL
The big, strong tail was the most flexible part of the body.

NOSTRILS
The nostrils were high up on the snout, to make it easier for the whale to breathe when it surfaced.

HINDLIMBS
The creature had a tiny set of hindlimbs two-thirds of the way along its length. These may have been used as claspers during mating.

TEETH
The teeth were pointed at the front of the jaw, and saw-edged towards the rear.

This massive, primitive whale had a large, flexible body and strong flippers. It cruised through the prehistoric oceans, snapping up marine creatures with its long jaws. *Basilosaurus* was unable to survive on land and almost certainly carried out all its activities in water, including courting, mating and giving birth.

Tiny hindlimbs visible towards its rear give clues as to the creature's ancient ancestry. It was descended from beasts that lived on land.

HOW
BIG WAS
IT?

A hopeful young male *Basilosaurus* has managed to attract two females. But, before he can mate, a larger, more aggressive male swims into view.

1

Older and bigger, the aggressive male is also intent on mating. He forcefully drives the young male away with painful bites on the flippers and tail.

2

DINO FACTS

LENGTH	15–25m
SKULL	Up to 1.5m
WEIGHT	At least 6 tonnes
PREY	Fish, crabs and, at lower depths, squid
WEAPONS	Huge jaws and sharp teeth

Basilosaurus probably ranged throughout all the world's oceans and seas in the Eocene epoch. Fossil remains have been found as far afield as Egypt and Alabama, Mississippi and Louisiana in southern USA.

Did You Know?

● The title *Basilosaurus* is rather inaccurate. It means 'king of the lizards', and was coined after the first discoveries of its fossil bones were presumed to belong to a giant reptile. The creature's alternative name, *Zeuglodon*, is more accurate – it refers to the animal's saw teeth.

● *Basilosaurus* bones were once fraudulently displayed as the remains of a legendary sea serpent.

● Primitive whales such as *Basilosaurus* may have evolved from an ancient group of meat-eating terrestrial mammals called the mesonychids. The skulls and teeth of these two groups have important similarities. Though they looked somewhat dog-like, the mesonychids were separate, in evolutionary terms, from modern-day carnivores.

DIATRYMA

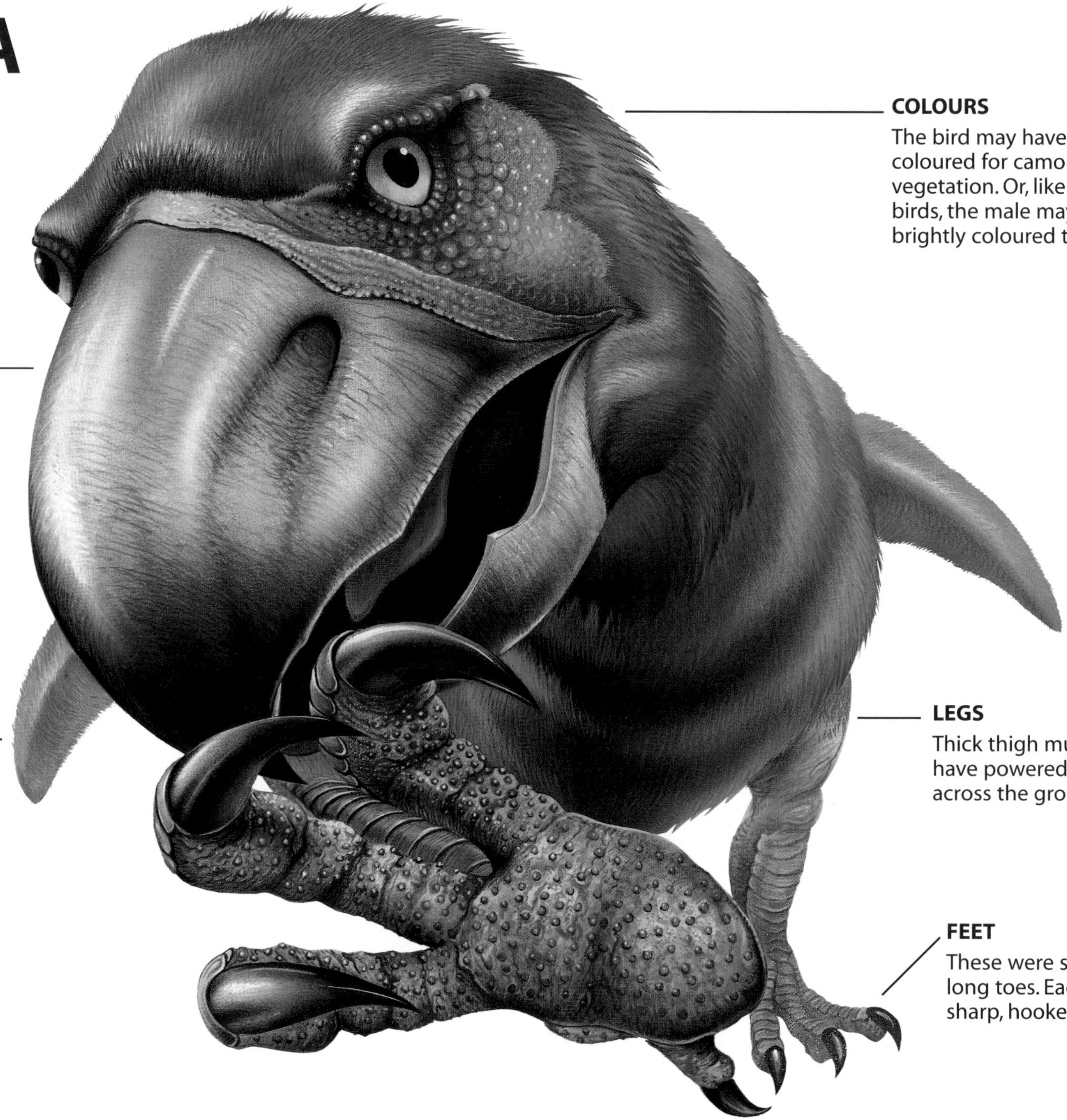

COLOURS

The bird may have been dully coloured for camouflage among vegetation. Or, like many modern birds, the male may have been brightly coloured to attract a mate.

BILL

Both parts were long, with sharp edges. The upper part had a pointed, curving tip.

WINGS

The stunted wings were not strong enough for flight. But they could have helped the bird keep its balance when running after terrified prey.

LEGS

Thick thigh muscles would have powered the great bird across the ground.

FEET

These were splayed, with four long toes. Each ended in a sharp, hooked talon.

One of the largest birds that ever set foot upon the Earth, *Diatryma* was a flightless, feathered giant. It was about as tall as an ostrich, but far bulkier in build, with sturdy legs and a huge head. It could easily have run down and butchered prey with its huge, hooked talons and bill. However, some experts think that it was not a killer at all, but a scavenger or even a plant-eater that used its bill to crop plants.

Diatryma stomped across North America and Europe 60–50 million years ago when the continents were still joined together, forming one large landmass.

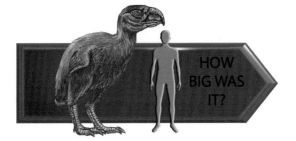

HOW BIG WAS IT?

DINO FACTS

HEIGHT	2m or more
WEIGHT	Probably 200kg
DIET	Experts think it hunted small animals; others that it scavenged carcasses or ate plants
WEAPONS	Big, powerful hooked bill and claws
MEANING OF NAME	'Terror crane'

Fossil remains of *Diatryma* have been found in New Jersey, Wyoming and New Mexico in the USA, and in England, Belgium and France in Europe. In *Diatryma*'s day, Europe and North America were joined.

Surprising a grazing *Hyracotherium* (prehistoric horse), the big bird pins it to the ground with a mighty foot.

1

The horse struggles to free itself, but there is no escaping *Diatryma*'s clutches. The bird puts the creature out of its misery with a single spine-snapping bite.

2

Did You Know?

● Giant birds similar to *Diatryma* survived much longer in South America. The fearsome-looking, flightless *Phororhacos* was still at large 20 million years ago. It stood about 1.5m tall and, like *Diatryma*, brandished a viciously hooked bill.

● Scientists believe the closest living relatives of *Diatryma* and its relatives are the birds known as the Gruiformes, an order that includes the coots, bustards and cranes.

● An almost complete fossil skeleton of *Diatryma* is on display in the American Museum of Natural History, in New York City, USA.

3

Diatryma's bill rips into its prey, snapping bones like matchwood. It eagerly starts tearing into its fresh and bloody innards.

ARGENTAVIS

WINGS
The huge wings could use every breath of wind to stay aloft.

BILL
The sharp, hooked bill could slice through a victim's hide like a great meat cleaver.

RUFF
Some experts think the bird had a ruff of neck feathers to guard it against the icy air.

TALONS
Powerful claws let the bird carry large prey back to the nest or hold a carcass steady while tearing off chunks of flesh.

LEGS
With its long, powerful legs, the bird could use a short take-off run to get into the air.

The biggest flying bird that ever lived, *Argentavis* was large enough to crush its prey to death as it landed. It would use its vicious hooked bill and claws to tear off chunks of meat.

This mighty hunter once patrolled the skies over Argentina. Its seven-metre wingspan could have kept it airborne for hours as it scoured the ground below looking for its next meal. Experts think that it preyed on living animals, but its diet probably also included the flesh of carcasses spotted from the air.

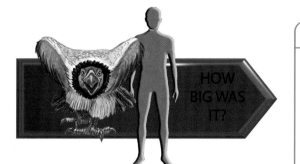

HOW BIG WAS IT?

DINO FACTS

HEIGHT	Up to 1.5m	Fossil *Argentavis* bones have been found only in La Pampa Province, Patagonia, in Argentina. However, the remains of close relatives have been discovered in large numbers throughout much of North and South America. The plains of Patagonia are surrounded by mountains, which would have provided plenty of roosting and nesting sites for the big bird.
WEIGHT	About 80kg	
WINGSPAN	Up to 7.6m	
DIET	Animals, dead or alive	
MEANING OF NAME	'Magnificent bird of Argentina'	

1 The powerful bird targets a pony-like *Diadiaphorus* running with its herd. It swoops down on the animal. The force of the blow instantly breaks its back.

2 Circling high, the bird spots a dead animal and glides down to land nearby. The bird tears off a strip of flesh and starts to eat.

Did You Know?

● When *Argentavis* was alive, the Argentinian plains were lush with grass, providing plenty of food for the plant-eaters on which the huge bird feasted. As the climate changed and the plains became semi-desert, prey numbers fell drastically, spelling doom for *Argentavis* and its ilk.

● The early ancestors of modern birds had teeth and may have evolved from small dinosaurs. They vanished, along with the dinosaurs, 65 million years ago, and were replaced by bird forms that resemble those found today.

● Birds reached their peak about one million years ago when, some experts say, there were well over 11,500 different species. Today there are about 9000 species, and many of them are at risk of extinction.

BORHYAENA

TAIL

The tail was thick at the base and could have supported the animal when it stood on its hindlegs – a feature common to marsupials.

TEETH

The teeth grew constantly, as they wore away or fell out.

LEGS

The muscular legs were strong enough to allow the hunter to chase prey for a short distance and spring on to the victim's back.

CLAWS

Its sharp claws were curved like a sabre for slashing power.

Borhyaena was a muscular, wolf-sized hunter living in Argentina in South America. At that time South America was an island, cut off from the rest of the world.

The top predator of its time, it may have lurked in long grass to ambush its prey, killing victims with one bite of its massive jaws. It may also have feasted on the carcasses of animals killed by other meat-eaters.

Borhyaena was a marsupial (pouched mammal), more closely related to a wallaby than a wolf. But its bone-crunching, meat-slicing teeth show clearly that it liked to dine on blood-soaked flesh.

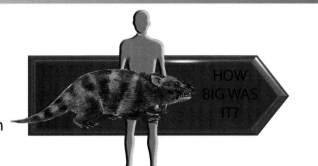

HOW BIG WAS IT?

DINO FACTS

LENGTH	Up to 1.5m	Remains of *Borhyaena* have so far been found only in Patagonia, a region of Argentina. However, the animal may have been more widespread in South America than the limited fossil evidence suggests. The remains of various other species of borhyaenid – the group of meat-eating marsupials to which *Borhyaena* belongs – have been found throughout the continent.
WEIGHT	90–100kg	
WEAPONS	Claws and powerful jaws	
DIET	Animals, dead or alive	
MEANING OF NAME	'Glutton hyena'	

1 A *Borhyaena* approaches the carcass of a plant-eater. Another *Borhyaena* is at the kill already, pulling at a leg. The newcomer joins in, and together they tear off the limb.

Did You Know?

● North and South America were separated for millions of years and therefore the marsupial mammals on the southern continent had little or no competition. But then, when the two continents reconnected, placental mammals invaded southwards from the north and competed for food with marsupials such as *Borhyaena*, resulting in the extinction of most of them.

● Experts think that marsupials evolved in the Americas and spread to Australia at a time when these continents were linked by land via Antarctica. Once Australia broke away from Antarctica, marsupial mammals there evolved into a wide variety of plant- and meat-eating species, many of which are still found there today, including such familiar creatures as kangaroos.

2 The two animals tug at the leg until one pulls the meat free from the other's jaws. It runs off to enjoy its feast alone.

BRONTOTHERIUM

NECK

Brontotherium's huge hump of a neck contained powerful muscles. These were needed to support its heavy headgear.

HORN

The male's enormous, Y-shaped 'horn' was formed of solid bone. It was covered with a layer of thick skin.

LEGS

The legs were stout and pillar-like, built to support the great creature's immense bulk.

BRAIN

The brain was probably only about the size of an orange and fairly smooth, making *Brontotherium* even less intelligent than a modern rhinoceros.

*B*rontotherium may look hideous to us, but what it lacked in brains and beauty it certainly made up for in bulk. In its day, this huge, rhinoceros-like creature was one of the biggest land mammals in North America. The males were bulky beasts that used their huge, bony horns to batter rivals. The toughest individuals won the right to mate with females.

Brontotherium appears to have roamed in herds through woodland, browsing on leaves. It probably used its rubbery lips to tear off each mouthful, then crushed food with its big cheek teeth. They became extinct when the climate changed and woods gave way to grass.

Did You Know?

● At the time when *Brontotherium* roamed North America, the Rocky Mountains were just being created. The area was intensely volcanic and, occasionally, eruptions would bury herds of *Brontotheriums* in clouds of hot ash – which is where many of their skeletons are found today.

● The brontotheres are sometimes called titanotheres, after the Titans: powerful early gods of Greek myth.

● Several Brontops skeletons have broken ribs, and, as far as we know, no other animal existed at this time that could have inflicted such injuries – supporting the view that the large brontotheres fought each other.

● Professor Marsh (1831–1899) of Yale University was the first person to study the brontotheres in detail.

HOW BIG WAS IT?

1 It is the mating season, and, as a smaller female *Brontotherium* waits nearby, two burly males charge head to head.

DINO FACTS

HEIGHT	Up to 2.5m at shoulder	*Brontotherium* lived in woodlands that once covered much of North America. Its remains are commonly found at the edges of plateaus in areas of previous mountain-building, such as the Badlands of Nebraska and South Dakota. Other brontotheres lived in northern Eurasia, migrating between the two landmasses by way of the Bering Straits (then a dry land bridge).
WEIGHT	Up to 4.5 tonnes	
DIET	Tender leaves and twigs	
WEAPONS	Male had big Y-shaped horn	
MEANING OF NAME	'Thunder beast'	

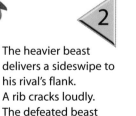

2 The heavier beast delivers a sideswipe to his rival's flank. A rib cracks loudly. The defeated beast staggers away in pain.

MEGALODON

SNOUT
This probably held sensors to detect scents and vibrations given out by prey.

PECTORAL FINS
Long fins would have acted rather like wings. The shark would have twisted them to steer itself up and down in the water.

TEETH
The teeth were huge, triangular saw-edged blades They had deep, thick roots for extra strength.

TAIL
Megalodon must have had a tall tail fin to power itself through the sea.

Megalodon was a killer of awesome ferocity. It was without doubt the most terrifying shark that has ever lived. Armed with teeth like saw-edged axe-blades, it could kill a great whale instantly, crushing it with one single bite.

Megalodon was probably the top predator in the world's seas for more than 20 million years. Yet between 3 million and 1 million years ago, its long, savage reign ended. Exactly why is a mystery. Maybe the great shark just ran out of food. Or perhaps it simply could not survive the bitterly cold temperatures of the Ice Age seas.

1 Tasting blood in the water, *Megalodon* homes in on a whale and its baby calf. Exhausted from giving birth, the whale is helpless to escape.

2 *Megalodon* slams into the whale and clamps its massive jaws around her ribcage. Her end is mercifully quick, but the calf's ordeal has only just begun.

DINO FACTS

LENGTH	17m or more
WEIGHT	25 tonnes or more
PREY	Whales and big fish
WEAPONS	Colossal saw-edged teeth
MEANING OF NAME	'Big-toothed shark'

Megalodon fossils have been found from the Americas and Europe to New Zealand and Australia. This suggests the shark lived in warm seas all around the world.

HOW BIG WAS IT?

Did You Know?

● Based on occasional claimed sightings of enormous sharks in the Pacific, some monster hunters think that *Megalodon* still lives!

● For centuries, people thought fossil *Megalodon* teeth were snake tongues magically turned to stone. Bernard Plissy, the 16th-century French scientist, was one of the first to realize the truth. But it was not until 1835 that the discovery became official, when the Swiss naturalist Louis Agassiz named the shark.

● The biggest *Megalodon* teeth are eagerly sought by collectors and fetch mega-prices. The rarest, most valuable ones are those in perfect condition – especially ones from phosphate pits, as these can be a beautiful red, white, orange or blue, rather than the usual grey and black.

PLATYBELODON

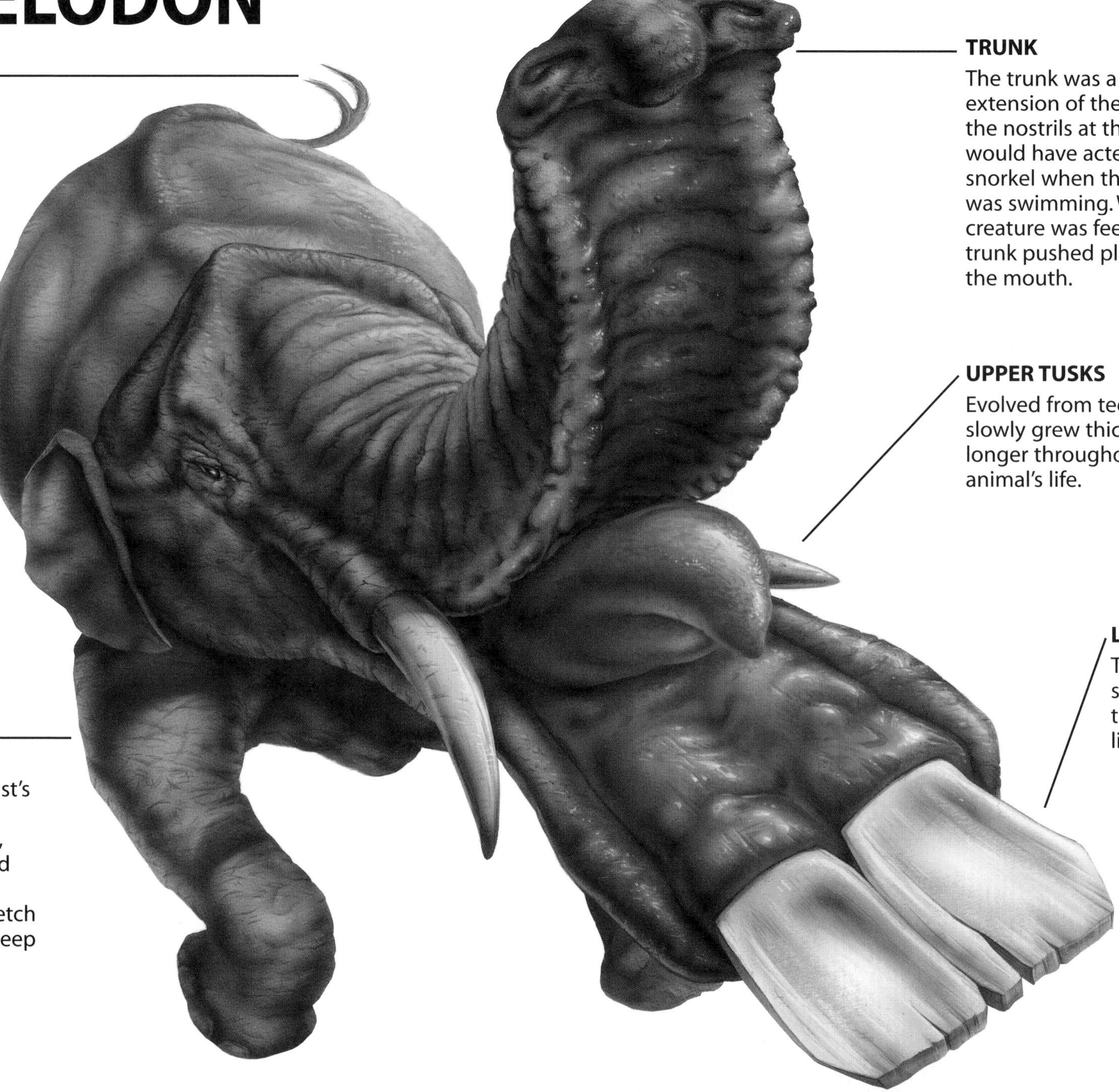

TAIL

Like modern elephants, *Platybelodon* would have used this to swat away biting flying insects.

TRUNK

The trunk was a flexible extension of the nose, with the nostrils at the tip. This would have acted as a snorkel when the animal was swimming. When the creature was feeding, the trunk pushed plants into the mouth.

UPPER TUSKS

Evolved from teeth, these slowly grew thicker and longer throughout the animal's life.

LOWER INCISORS

These would have sliced cleanly through thick roots, like a garden spade.

LEGS

Pillar-like legs supported the beast's great weight. Like modern elephants, *Platybelodon* would have swum dog-paddle when a stretch of water was too deep to wade across.

This ancient relative of the elephant had a huge, shovel-like lower jaw. It used its sharp-edged teeth to scoop up and slice off great mouthfuls of luscious wetland plants. *Platybelodon* roamed worldwide in browsing herds, devouring enormous amounts of vegetation every day.

If any predator dared to attack this massive creature, it would have had the short, downward-curving tusks in *Platybelodon*'s upper jaw to avoid. These were not used for gathering food, but they would have made formidable weapons.

The only elephants living today are the African and Asian kinds, but, in *Platybelodon*'s day, there were many different types.

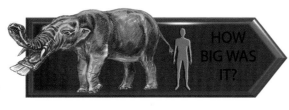

HOW BIG WAS IT?

Anancus lived in the forests of Europe and Asia at the same time as *Platybelodon* was around. It had straight tusks up to 4m long, to dig for juicy tubers.

1

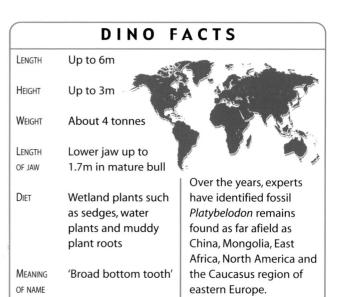

Ambelodon was a close relative of *Platybelodon*. It had a narrow, 1m-long lower jaw and teeth for scooping up plants from rivers.

3

Cuvieronius roamed the Americas until only 1600 years ago. It had weird spiral tusks and may have gored many of the men who hunted it to extinction.

2

DINO FACTS

LENGTH	Up to 6m
HEIGHT	Up to 3m
WEIGHT	About 4 tonnes
LENGTH OF JAW	Lower jaw up to 1.7m in mature bull
DIET	Wetland plants such as sedges, water plants and muddy plant roots
MEANING OF NAME	'Broad bottom tooth'

Over the years, experts have identified fossil *Platybelodon* remains found as far afield as China, Mongolia, East Africa, North America and the Caucasus region of eastern Europe.

Did You Know?

● One of *Platybelodon*'s ancestors was 2.5m-high *Phiomia*, which lived in Africa 30 million years ago. It had a top lip like a 'proto-trunk', which worked with its long lower jaw and teeth to gather lush forest foliage. *Phiomia* means 'lake province beast', in reference to the Fayum area of Egypt where its remains were found.

● The fact that *Platybelodon* lived in both North America and Asia shows that there was once a land bridge across the narrow Bering Straits.

● Experts found bones of an unborn baby *Platybelodon* inside an adult female unearthed in Mongolia.

THYLACOSMILUS

EYES
Thylacosmilus must have had keen binocular vision to judge its attacks precisely.

BODY
The stocky, muscular build was suited for ambush, not for chasing prey.

SABRE TEETH
These sprouted from long canals that ran through the skull to behind the eyes.

LEGS
The beast had strong legs and sharp claws for clinging to struggling prey.

SHEATHS
These guarded the sabre teeth and stopped the animal stabbing itself.

More than two million years ago, this terrifying beast prowled the plains of South America. It could rip out the throats of rhinoceros-size victims with its sabre-like teeth, then carve them up to feed its family. *Thylacosmilus* was no larger than a leopard, but it was able to kill animals much bigger than itself by stabbing them in the throat with its colossal teeth.

Thylacosmilus looked like a sabre-toothed cat, but it was actually a marsupial, like modern-day kangaroos. It needed sabre teeth because it preyed on thick-skinned plant-eaters. The only way to kill such animals was to slice through a main artery, and sabre teeth were ideal for the job.

Did You Know?

● *Thylacosmilus* died out 2 million years ago, probably because it could not compete with sabre-toothed cats invading South America from North America after major volcanic eruptions joined the two continents. One reason for this may have been that sabre-toothed cats bred more successfully than *Thylacosmilus*, but no one knows for sure.

● The sabre-toothed cat *Smilodon* survived until 10,000 years ago, when it seems it was wiped out by the spears and traps of hunters.

● Many modern-day marsupials, including a marsupial mole and marsupial cats, resemble 'normal' non-pouched mammals. There was even a marsupial 'wolf', called the *thylacine*, until it was hunted to extinction early in the 20th century.

HOW BIG WAS IT?

A female *Thylacosmilus* with a litter of hungry cubs to feed waits by a waterhole. Eventually her patience is rewarded. A thirsty *Telicomys* comes down for a drink.

1

DINO FACTS		
LENGTH	Up to 1.5m	Remains of *Thylacosmilus* have been found on the pampas of Argentina. The beast roamed these plains just over 2 million years ago, in the late Miocene and early Pliocene epochs at the very end of the Tertiary period. At this time the whole region was probably very much the way it is today: mainly hot, dry and dusty open grasslands, with very few trees.
PREY	Big, tough-skinned plant-eating mammals	
WEAPONS	Two sabre-like teeth up to 13cm long	
MEANING OF NAME	'Pouch knife'	

Leaping from her hiding place, she sinks her lethal sabre teeth deep into its neck. Slicing downwards, the teeth cut straight through a main artery.

2

The *Telicomys* collapses from blood loss. The *Thylacosmilus* cubs come out to share in a hearty meal with their mother.

3

COLOSSOCHELYS

SHELL
The massive upper shell, would have been covered with a beautiful layer of tortoiseshell, just like on modern tortoises.

UNDERSIDE
The armour continued beneath the belly. Even if the tortoise were overturned, there would still be no way in.

LEGS
Colossochelys had strong, sturdy legs to lift its massive body off the ground. Even so, it would have been a slow mover.

FEET
The soles of *Colossochelys'* feet had thick, cushioning pads, to help spread its great weight.

BEAK
The horny beak was perfect for slicing leaves and twigs off low-growing plants. The tortoise might also snap up the occasional worm.

CLAWS
The beast had sharp claws to dig a nest for its eggs.

The heavyweight champion of the tortoise world, *Colossochelys* roamed the Earth over a million years ago, safe inside an enormously tough, thick shell. It was by far the largest tortoise the world has ever seen: it was twice as big as giant tortoises alive today.

Colossochelys was a slow-moving, gentle giant that spent its days munching peaceably on grass and other low-lying plants. The tortoise survived due to the thick coat of armour on its back. With this for protection, it could escape from even the most fearsome and agile predators.

HOW BIG WAS IT?

While feeding quietly, *Colossochelys* spots another animal approaching. The creature is a hungry sabre-toothed cat.

1

DINO FACTS

LENGTH	2.5m	The best-preserved *Colossochelys* remains to date were found in the Siwalik Hills of northern India, at the feet of the vast Himalayan mountain range. Shell remnants of other ancient tortoises believed by scientists to belong to this genus have turned up in Myanmar (Burma), Java, Sulawesi and Timor.
HEIGHT	1m	
WEIGHT	850kg	
DIET	Leaves and shoots	
MEANING OF NAME	'Colossal shell'	

Did You Know?

● *Colossochelys* is also known by another Latin name: *Testudo atlas*. In Greek mythology, Atlas was the Titan (giant god) who held up the world.

● Although *Colossochelys* was the biggest tortoise ever, it was not the largest shelled reptile. That title goes to *Archelon*, a truly monstrous sea turtle that lived at the same time as the dinosaurs. This beast grew to more than 3.7m long and weighed more than 2 tonnes.

● The smallest living tortoise is the speckled Cape tortoise from the far south-west of Africa. A full-grown adult, just 9cm long and weighing only 300g, would fit in your hand. It would take nearly 3000 speckled Cape tortoises in a pile to outweigh a single *Colossochelys*.

2

As the sabre-toothed cat attempts to make the kill, *Colossochelys* withdraws its head and legs into its massive shell. Nothing is left exposed.

3

Foiled, the cat hops onto the shell to groom itself. The tortoise will have to wait until the cat grows bored before it can relax.

DOEDICURUS

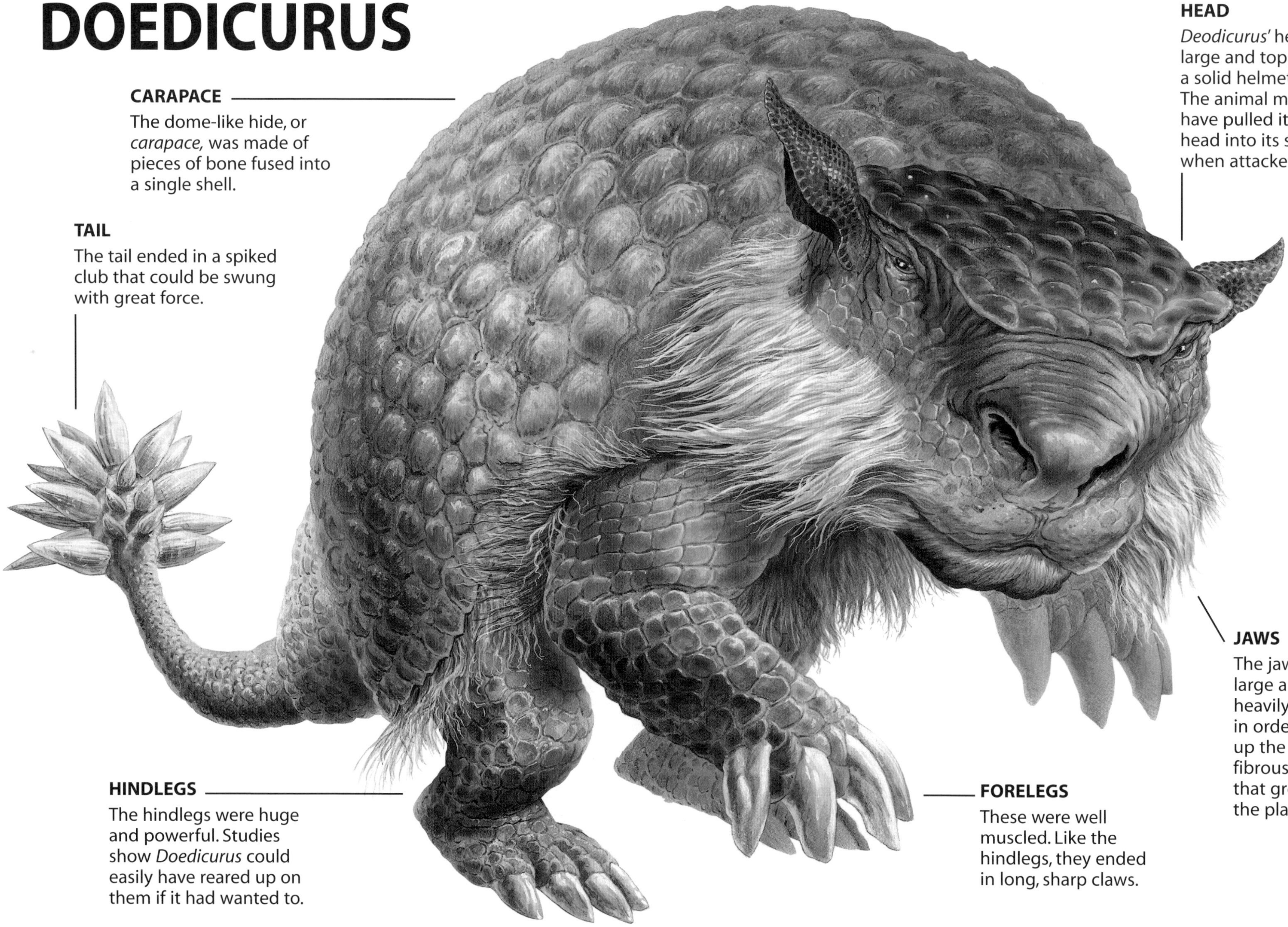

HEAD

Deodicurus' head was large and topped with a solid helmet of bone. The animal may have pulled its head into its shell when attacked.

CARAPACE

The dome-like hide, or *carapace,* was made of pieces of bone fused into a single shell.

TAIL

The tail ended in a spiked club that could be swung with great force.

JAWS

The jaws were large and heavily muscled in order to grind up the tough, fibrous grasses that grew on the plains.

HINDLEGS

The hindlegs were huge and powerful. Studies show *Doedicurus* could easily have reared up on them if it had wanted to.

FORELEGS

These were well muscled. Like the hindlegs, they ended in long, sharp claws.

This powerful beast was one of the most heavily armoured and well-armed mammals that have ever lived. Almost its entire body was encased in horn-covered bone, with a terrifying spiky club on its tail. If ever it got angry, only another *Doedicurus* would have dared to hang around for a fight.

Doedicurus belonged to a group of armoured mammals called glyptodonts that roamed the Americas for almost 20 million years. Glyptodonts were plant-eaters that specialized in eating tough grasses. Their diet was reflected in their jaws and teeth. They had unusual-shaped grinding molars and deep jaw bones.

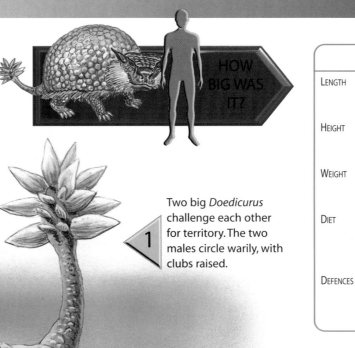

HOW BIG WAS IT?

1 Two big *Doedicurus* challenge each other for territory. The two males circle warily, with clubs raised.

2 Then the fight starts. Blow after blow lands on their armoured hides, but without leaving a mark. Finally, stunned by a blow to the head, one backs away.

DINO FACTS

LENGTH	Up to 4m	*Doedicurus* remains were found in Patagonia, a region of South America. Patagonia has been a treasure trove of mammal fossils, including those of other glyptodonts, as well as the remains of early birds and dinosaurs. *Doedicurus* roamed the pampas, or grasslands, of the Pleistocene age. Today, the pampas covers much of Argentina and southern Brazil.
HEIGHT	1.2m	
WEIGHT	Up to 2 tonnes	
DIET	Probably grasses and roots	
DEFENCES	All-over body armour; spiked tail club	

Did You Know?

● *Doedicurus* died out less than 10,000 years ago and may still have been around when humans moved into South America. Natives still tell stories about creatures that sound just like this armoured giant.

● Scientists think that *Doedicurus* would have moved quite quickly, despite the weight of its armour. Their calculations show that it could have galloped as fast as a modern buffalo – at more than 30km/h.

● *Doedicurus* was one of the last of a long line of glyptodonts; early species were only the size of a domestic cat. The giants evolved 15 million years later.

● The name *Doedicurus* means 'armoured tail' – an understatement to describe such a scary weapon.

HOMOTHERIUM

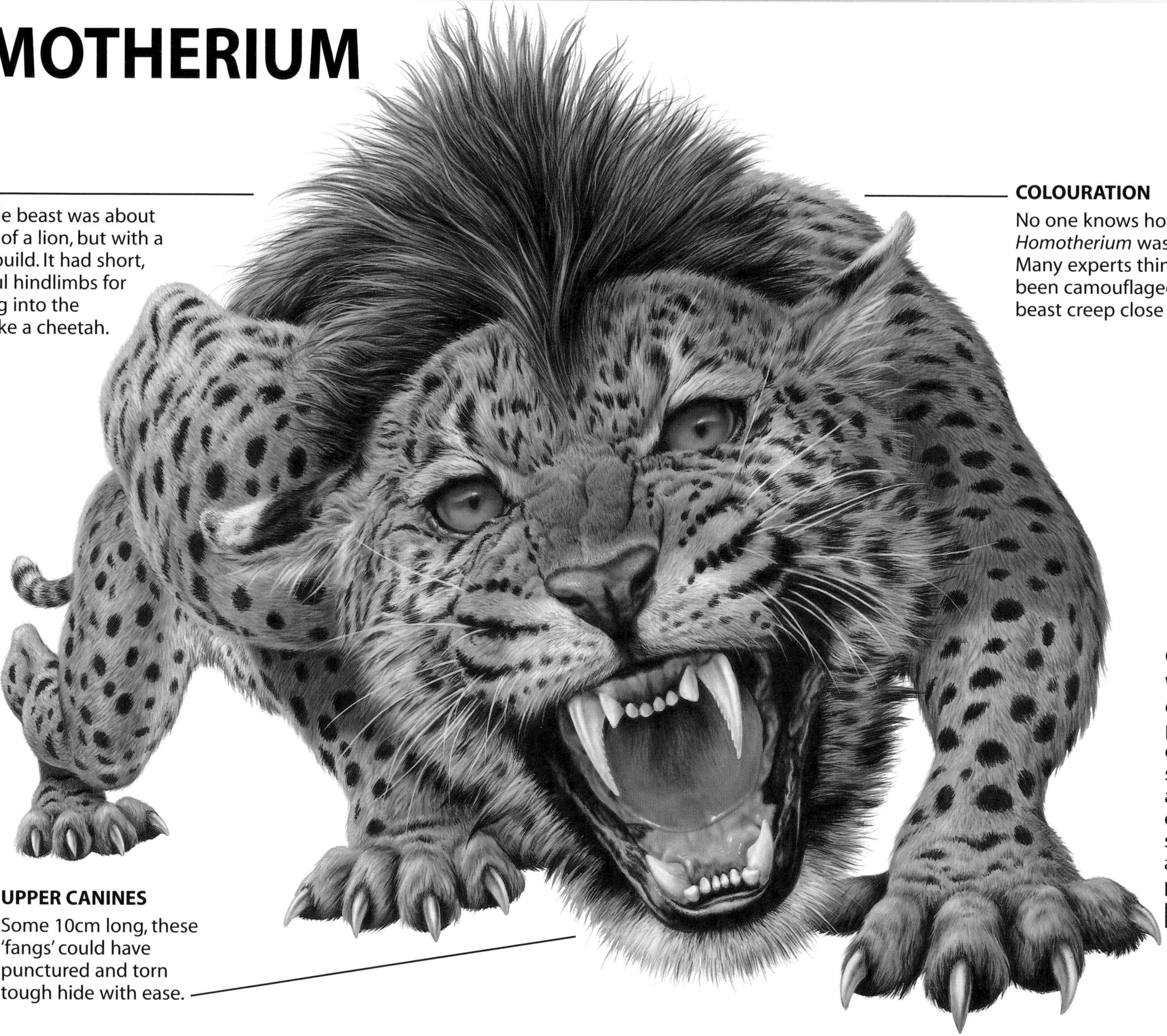

BUILD

This agile beast was about the size of a lion, but with a lighter build. It had short, powerful hindlimbs for sprinting into the attack like a cheetah.

COLOURATION

No one knows how the coat of *Homotherium* was coloured. Many experts think it would have been camouflaged to help the beast creep close to prey.

CLAWS

With one swipe of a clawed paw, the cat could have slashed open a mammoth calf's belly, spilling blood and guts in profusion.

UPPER CANINES

Some 10cm long, these 'fangs' could have punctured and torn tough hide with ease.

Homotherium was a ferocious cat with sharp, curved teeth. The cats slaughtered prey almost worldwide until only 10,000 years ago. Like a cheetah, it would have bounded into the attack with an amazing spurt of speed over short distances. It had a keen appetite and often butchered prey much larger than itself, including baby mammoths.

The remains of 13 *Homotherium* cubs and 20 adults found in a cave in Texas, USA, indicate that the cat lived in groups, like lions. The cave also yielded the tooth-marked bones of between 300 and 400 mammoth calves. This suggests that the adult cats slaughtered them and dragged them back to feed their cubs.

Did You Know?

● *Homotherium* lived during the last Ice Age and may have evolved such adaptations to a cold climate as white fur, small ears and large, thickly padded paws, much like the Himalayan snow leopard today.

● From analysis of *Homotherium*'s skeletal structure, experts have deduced that the creature probably had a top running speed of 60km/h.

● Some bone boffins believe that a prehistoric stone carving of a big cat discovered in the cave of Isturitz in south-western France depicts a *Homotherium*. Marks on the cat in question indicate spotted fur.

● Most experts agree that, in addition to attacking large prey, *Homotherium* would have scavenged any animal carcass it came across.

HOW BIG WAS IT?

DINO FACTS

LENGTH	1–1.5m
WEIGHT	Up to 230kg
PREY	Plant-eating mammals
WEAPONS	Sharp, curved canines
MEANING OF NAME	'Same beast'

Remains of different *Homotherium* species have been unearthed at various sites in Europe, Asia, Africa and North America, but the beast appears to have been most common in Europe.

Two female *Homotherium* launch a brutal assault on a mammoth calf. They rake terrible wounds in its throat and flanks with their teeth and claws. **1**

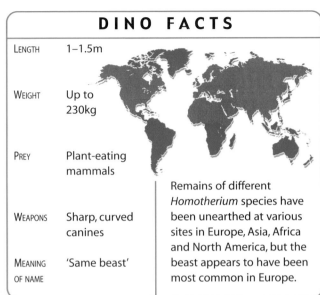

2 Hearing the calf's cries, the adult mammoths come running. As the cats watch from a safe distance, the calf's mother tries to rouse it with her trunk. But it is too late – the calf is dead.

3 With great reluctance, the mammoths eventually abandon the body and move away. The cats return to feast greedily before shearing off chunks to take to the cubs.

SMILODON

FORELIMBS

The huge forelimbs were immensely powerful. The shoulder joints rose high above the body.

BODY

Smilodon had a bobbed tail, short legs and a stocky body, not the build of a runner. It probably waited in ambush, then pounced on bigger animals.

JAWS

The jaws opened to an angle of 120°, nearly twice the gape of a lion.

CANINES

Chopping down with its tusk-like teeth, *Smilodon* could cut through the toughest animal hide.

CLAWS

Each paw was armed with sharp claws for gripping struggling prey.

With flesh-ripping claws, rippling muscles and a blood-curdling roar, this fierce cat must have terrified the earliest humans. *Smilodon* could open its jaws to an incredible angle and stab its teeth into flesh like twin pick-axes. These teeth were so long they stuck out like tusks when *Smilodon* closed its mouth.

Smilodon was not built for speed and probably specialized in ambushing large, lumbering herbivores such as bison and mammoths. It would have sprung from its cover and killed its victim with repeated stabbing blows from its long, terrible teeth.

HOW BIG WAS IT?

DINO FACTS

LENGTH	1.2–1.5m	
HEIGHT	90cm to shoulder	
WEIGHT	200kg	Members of the *Smilodon* genus lived across most of North and South America during the span of the last Ice Age, from about 2.5 million years to 10,000 years ago. Fossils suggest that there were at least three types in existence.
PREY	Large mammals	
MEANING OF NAME	'Knife tooth'	

A mammoth fails to notice *Smilodon* lying in wait. With a mighty pounce, the big cat springs from cover. Clamping hold with sharp claws, the cat bites repeatedly at the victim's throat.

1

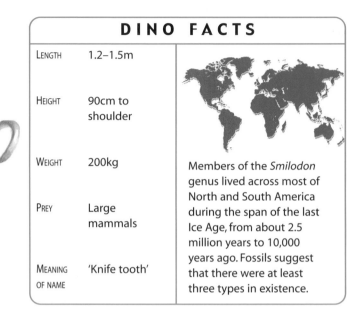

The mammoth reels in pain and shock from the cat's slashing blows. Finally, it sinks to the ground, and *Smilodon* gnaws greedily at its flesh.

2

Did You Know?

● Although strong, *Smilodon's* 18cm canines occasionally broke during struggles with prey – especially if they became stuck fast in bone. One fossil wolf was even discovered with a length of *Smilodon* tooth embedded in its skull.

● So many impressive *Smilodon* remains have been recovered from the La Brea site in Los Angeles that the big cat has been adopted as California's official state fossil.

● *Smilodon* was the most recent of several types of sabre-toothed cats. *Megantereon*, a probable ancestor of *Smilodon*, spread from Eurasia into the Americas between 3 and 2 million years ago. But a separate group of 'false' sabre-toothed cats emerged much earlier on, about 40 million years ago.

WOOLLY MAMMOTH

HEAD
The adult's domed head provided extra anchorage for the tendons in the back that held up the heavy-tusked skull.

TUSKS
Massive, curved tusks grew throughout the mammoth's life. These fearsome weapons were often used to fight predators. They also made useful tools for digging and clearing snow.

TRUNK
The mammoth used its trunk to feed on a wide variety of vegetation.

BODY
As the mammoth grew, it developed a shoulder hump and a sloping back.

EARS
The ears were rounded, like ours. They were small to reduce heat loss. An elephant's ears are much larger.

FUR
A dense, woolly coat provided insulation against the cold.

FEET
Even the feet were hairy. They had wide soles and a spongy pad that cushioned the weight of the mammoth's great body.

The majestic woolly mammoth walked the Earth for almost a quarter of a million years. It is named after its dense covering of insulating hair, which enabled it to survive the cold of the last Ice Age. It was armed with heavy, twisting tusks that grew up to four metres long, which it used both for fighting and foraging.

It was a familiar animal to the Ice Age hunters, who hunted the woolly mammoth for its meat. They also drew its image on their cave walls and carved its ivory tusks into magical emblems. In more recent times, its thawed remains continued to amaze all those who came across its great bulk.

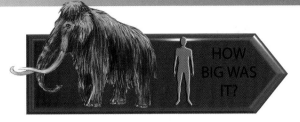

HOW BIG WAS IT?

MAMMOTH MEAL

A woolly mammoth would provide a Stone Age community with meat for weeks. But butchering the carcass was a huge task. One way of tackling the problem was to cook the dead beast on the spot. They probably hacked open its chest cavity, lit a fire inside the ribcage, and waited for the insides to roast. They also collected the tusks and larger bones to use as building materials and weapons.

DINO FACTS

HEIGHT	2.6–3.5m at shoulder
TUSKS	Up to 4.2m long
WEIGHT	Up to 6 tonnes
DIET	Grass, moss, small shrubs and leaves
LIFESPAN	Probably up to 60 years

Probably originating in Siberia, woolly mammoths spread across the northern world, colonizing a wide sweep of territory in Europe and Asia and crossing the Ice Age region of Berengia (now the Bering Straits) to enter North America.

Did You Know?

● Mammoth bones began to emerge from the thawing soil at the end of the Ice Age. Natives of Siberia thought these were the remains of giant mole–like creatures that occasionally surfaced – only to die on exposure to the sunlight.

● In 1557, a Swiss doctor settled a dispute about a pile of mammoth bones when he declared that they belonged to a human giant 5.5m tall.

● Fishermen in the North Sea often bring up mammoth teeth in their nets because this area was dry land at various times during the Ice Age, and is now rich in fossils and bones.

● In the early 20th century, some Siberian people thought mammoths still lived underground, causing earthquakes as they stomped about.

GLOSSARY

AMPHIBIAN

An animal that spends part of the time on land and part of the time in the water, such as a frog or a toad. Most amphibians have four legs and smooth, moist skin without scales.

ANKYLOSAUR

A type of well-armoured, plant-eating dinosaur. There were many different types of ankylosaur, but all had short, powerful legs and heavy armour.

AQUATIC

Living in or often found in water. Strictly speaking, dinosaurs only lived on land. However some dinosaur-like reptiles, such as the *Libonectes*, lived in water.

BIPED

An animal that walks on two legs. Humans are bipedal and some types of dinosaur, such as *Tyrannosaurus rex*, were also bipedal.

CAMOUFLAGE

Many creatures use special patterns or colours to help them blend into their surroundings and hide from prey or predators. This is called camouflage. No one knows exactly what colour the dinosaurs were, but many dinosaurs probably used camouflage patterns to help them hide. It is even possible that some were able to change colour like chameleons can today.

CARNIVORE

A meat-eating dinosaur, such as *Tyrannosaurus rex*, or any other meat-eating creature. Many carnivorous dinosaurs had sharp teeth or claws to help them kill and cut meat from their prey.

COLD BLOODED

Dinosaurs and other reptiles are cold blooded. This means that they do not produce their own body heat but take on the same temperature as their surroundings. They are cold and slow when the surroundings are cold, and warm and active when their surroundings are warm.

COUNTERBALANCE

To balance one weight against another. Many dinosaurs had long heavy tails to counterbalance the weight of their bodies.

CYNODONT

A group of mammal-like reptiles that lived in the later Permian to early Jurassic period. Although they were reptiles, cynodonts were not dinosaurs. The group probably included the ancestors of modern mammals.

DINOSAUR

Scientists use the word dinosaur to refer to a particular type of land-dwelling reptile that lived during the Triassic, Jurassic or Cretaceous period, but most people use the word to refer to any large, prehistoric reptile. The word means 'terrible lizard' in Greek.

EXOSKELETON

Some animals have a skeleton on the outside, instead of the inside, of their bodies. This is an exoskeleton. Animals with exoskeletons include insects and crabs. The trilobite, a very early type of animal, had an exoskeleton.

EXTINCTION

The disappearance of an entire species. Around 65 million years ago a great extinction killed the last of the dinosaurs.

This is why there are no dinosaurs alive today. More recently, creatures such as the dodo, a large flightless bird, have also become extinct.

FOSSIL

A plant, an animal or an animal track that has been preserved in rock. Usually, when an animal dies, its remains are completely destroyed over time. But sometimes the remains are buried before they disappear. Over time the earth or mud around the body turns into rock. Although the body disappears eventually, the impression of the creature is preserved in the rock forever. Most of our knowledge of dinosaurs comes from fossils.

HERBIVORE

A plant-eating dinosaur or other animal. Many plant-eating dinosaurs needed huge amounts of vegetation to get enough energy. They had huge stomachs to digest all the plant matter.

ICHTHYOSAUR

A group of large marine reptiles. The name ichthyosaur means 'fish lizard', but although the reptiles spent their whole lives in water, they breathed air, so they were more like modern whales than fish.

INCISOR TOOTH

One of the chisel-shaped cutting teeth found at the front of the mouth.

INVERTEBRATE

Any creature without a backbone, such as an insect or a jellyfish.

LIZARD

A long-bodied reptile, usually with two pairs of legs and a tail that becomes narrower towards the tip. A dinosaur is a type of lizard.

MAMMAL

A warm-blooded animal with a backbone and hairy skin. Mammals give birth to live young and feed their babies on milk.

MARSUPIAL

A type of mammal with a pouch to keep its young while they develop. Kangaroos and wallabies are both types of marsupials.

MOLAR TOOTH

One of the rounded or flattened teeth used for crushing, chewing or grinding.

PLANKTON

Tiny plants or animals that live in water and drift along in the currents.

PREDATOR

A dinosaur or other animal that hunts and kills other creatures.

PREHISTORIC

Before recorded (written) history. The word prehistoric can refer to many billions of years ago, long before any living creatures existed, or it can refer to a period only a few thousand years ago. Dinosaurs are called prehistoric because they lived millions of years ago.

REPTILE

A type of cold-blooded, air-breathing animal. Most reptiles lay eggs and have skin covered with scales or bony plates. Snakes, lizards, turtles, alligators and dinosaurs are all types of reptile.

SAURAPOD

A type of large plant-eating dinosaur. There were many different types of saurapod, but all had small heads, long necks and five toes. Some saurapods were larger than any other land animal.

SCAVENGER

A dinosaur or other animal that eats the dead remains of other creatures.

VERTEBRATE

Any creature with a backbone, including mammals, birds, fish and reptiles.

HOW TO PRONOUNCE DINOSAUR NAMES

Most dinosaurs are given Latin or Greek names, which can make them seem difficult to read or pronounce properly, but with a little bit of practice it's easy to get the hang of them. Try to read each name slowly and sound out the names one syllable at a time.

There are a few rules that may help you get used to the more unfamiliar names:

● Most vowels (including 'y') are pronounced short rather than long, as in words such as 'fish' or 'box'. For example, *Tyrannosaurus* = **Ti**-RAN-o-SAWR-us.

● Double vowels, such as 'oe' or 'ei' are pronounced long, as in words such as 'feel' and 'weight'. For example, *Ouranosaurus* = **Oo**-RAHN-o-SAWR-us.

● 'Ch' is pronounced as a hard 'k'. For example *Suchomimus* = **SOOK**-o-MIEM-us.

● 'Coe' is pronounced with a soft 'c', like in 'cent' and a long vowel sound, like in 'see'. For example, *Coelacanth* = **SEE**-la-kanth. *Coelophysis* = **SEEL**-o-FIE-sis.

● In names beginning with 'ps' or 'pt', the 'p' is silent. For example *Pteranodon* = **Ter**-AN-oh-don. *Psittacosaurus* = **SIT**-a-ko-SAWR-us.

Don't get discouraged if someone corrects your pronunciation – not everybody agrees on how Latin and Greek words should be pronounced anyway!

INDEX